SCIENCE
A MASTER FILE
KEY STAGE 1

Editors

D C Perkins, BA (Hons), MEd, PhD (Wales) and E J Perkins, BSc (Hons), MEd

Illustrations by Anthony James

These Master Files are designed for use in the classroom. Each consists of teachers' notes, pupils' resource material, worksheets, activities and record sheet. Each book covers a part of the national curriculum in depth allowing the teacher to decide the amount of material to use according to the age and ability of the children.

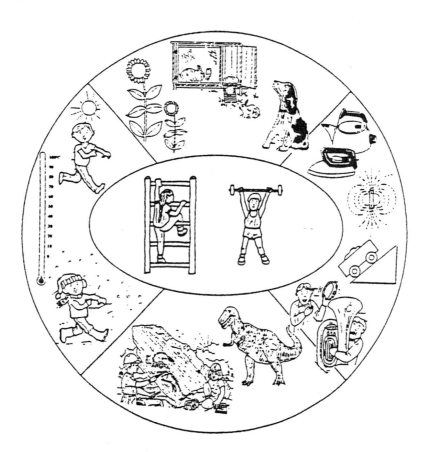

DOMINO BOOKS (WALES) LTD
SWANSEA SA1 1 FN
Tel. 01792 459378   Fax. 01792 466337
Science Master File KS1 © EJP & DCP 1995. Reprinted (twice) 1996, 1997, 1998, 1999
ISBN 1 85772 108 X

CONTENTS 1

PUPILS' RESOURCES/WORKSHEETS

CONTENTS 2

TEACHERS' NOTES AND RESOURCES

HOW TO USE YOUR MASTER FILE

For many experienced teachers these few lines will seem superfluous. This book follows the guidelines of the National Curriculum Order for Science. The science learned depends on the child's ability. By the end of Key Stage 1, most pupils should be able to cope with the material in Levels 1 to 3. By the end of Key Stage 2, they should be able to cope with the material in Levels 2 - 5. Some of the worksheets are more difficult than others. There is plenty of material that all will find interesting and fun to tackle and other work that is more challenging. We do not envisage any problems selecting appropriate material.

The scope of the material taught in science today has widened considerably and the emphasis on relating the subject to 'real' situations in the 'real' world makes the subject less mysterious and of more obvious use. A sound understanding of the fundamental theory is essential but so is an awareness that tedious repetition creates nothing but boredom. It is when children are little, when everything is new that the foundations of scientific ability are developed, interest generated or lost.

1. All the material in this book is photocopiable as defined on the first page. This means that all the material can be used in any way you wish in the classroom situation. Drawings can be photocopied and adapted for further work.

2. Covering sections of the master copies with plain paper enables resource material to be used in different ways. This is useful when it is felt that the material on one sheet should be used at different times especially with children who are slower at learning.

3. Reduction of the A4 master copies to A5 means that they can be pasted in children's exercise books. The master copies can also be enlarged to A3 making it easier for students to work on them as a group.

4. Some of the photocopies can be cut to make additional puzzles and games.

5. It is intended that the material should be used selectively depending on the ages and abilities of your pupils.

6. Much of the completed work may be used as visual aids around the classroom.

7. Remember, there are often several ways in which problems can be tackled.

8. Project work may be done individually, in groups and/or with teacher participation.

9. Science is increasingly important in everyday life. The disciplines leading to logical thinking are invaluable. Teaching children to question material presented to them, to plan their work, to hypothesise and then to test their theories are skills that will help them in their everyday work when they are adults. Good habits learned now will last.

10. Science is about discoveries and adventures. In the classroom today, children can develop the confidence and the skills they will need to deal with the science of tomorrow.

We hope you enjoy using this book and welcome any comments.

Living or non-living?

Colour the things that are alive.

flower

frog

sheep

snail

robot

snake

computer

snowman

dog

fish

woolly jumper

teddy

grass

bird

tadpoles

Materials

Colour the things which have been made from something that was once living.

bread

Dalek

wall

glass

book

plastic bottle

meat

jumper

quill

coin

horseshoe

chair

boat

carpet

football

Things needed by living things

Put a tick if living things need these.

	Animals	Plants	Humans
Air			
Water			
Food			
Sunlight			
To reproduce			
To move			
To excrete			
Soil			
Music			
Warmth			
Senses			

Things I can do

Draw lines to join the words that show what each person is doing.

weight lifting

climbing

handstands

running

watching

karate

diving

playing
football

swimming

jumping
on the
trampoline

What do you like doing best?

playing tennis

Movement

Draw lines to show how each animal moves. Some animals may be able to move in more than one way. You will need to draw two or more lines for these.

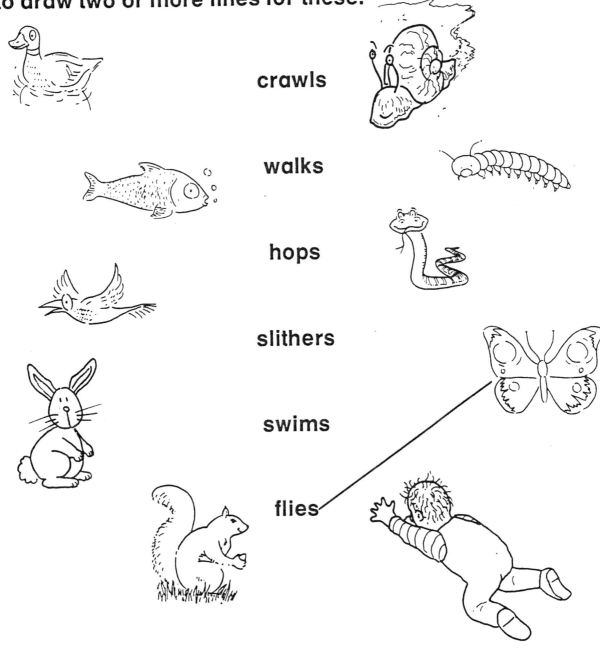

crawls

walks

hops

slithers

swims

flies

Draw an animal you like and say how it moves.

Parents and babies

Join the babies to their parents.

Fill the missing spaces choosing from these drawings.

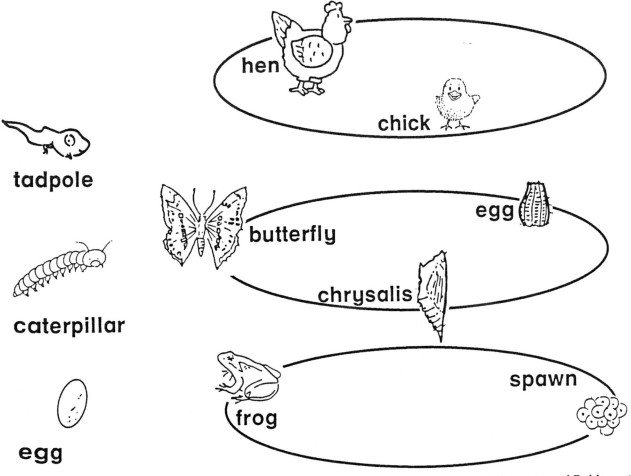

tadpole

caterpillar

egg

Where do they live?

Colour the picture and animals. Then cut out the animals and paste them in the picture.

Me

Draw lines to join the words to the parts of your body.

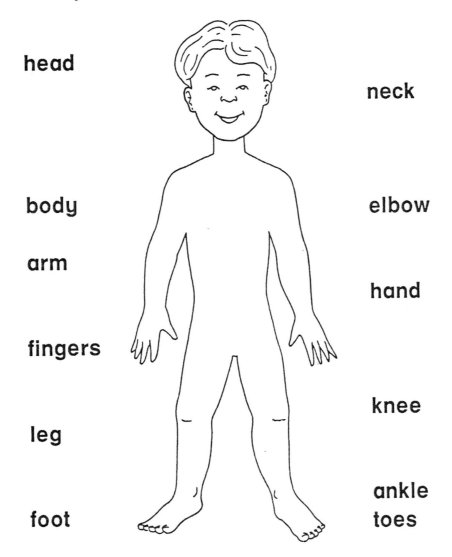

head

neck

body

elbow

arm

hand

fingers

knee

leg

ankle

foot

toes

Look in a mirror and draw and colour your face.

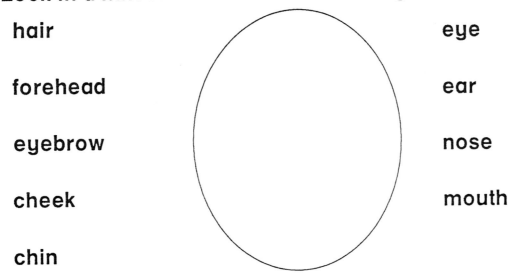

hair

eye

forehead

ear

eyebrow

nose

cheek

mouth

chin

Draw lines to join the words to the right parts.

Is your face happy or sad? How do you know?

My family album

Draw and colour pictures of some of the members of your family.

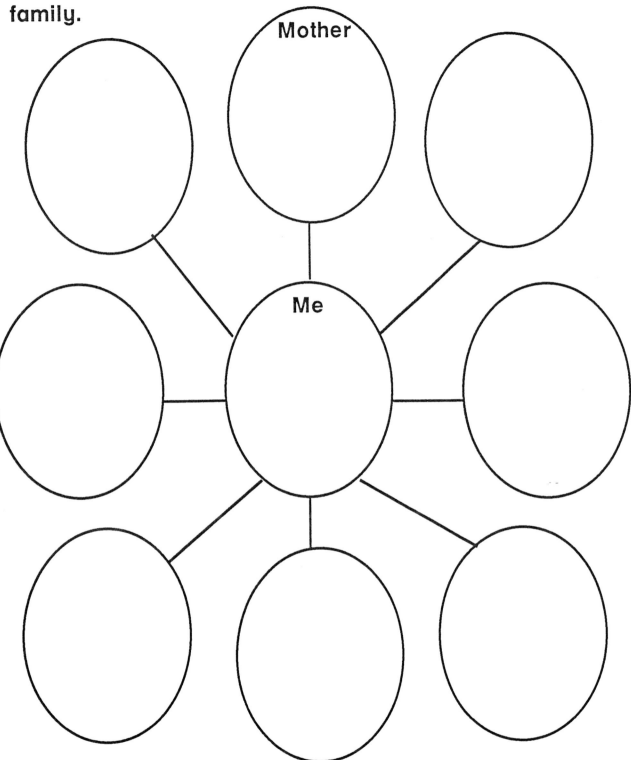

Mother

Me

Who do you look like in your family?
Who has the same colour eyes as you?
Who has the same colour hair as you?
Who do you think you will look like when you grow up?
Make models of your family out of plasticine or playdough.

Hands and feet

Put left and right on these drawings. How many fingers are there on each hand?
Draw lines to join the gloves to the correct hands.

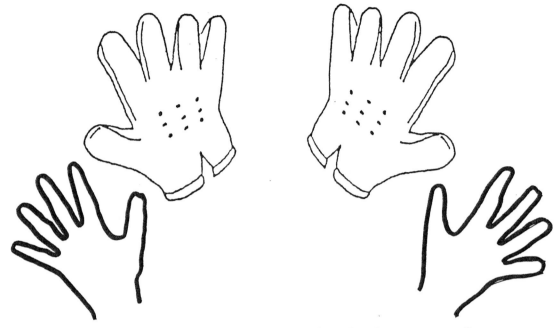

Draw around your hands. Are both the same?
Write left and right on the drawings of your hands.

Put left and right on these drawings. How many toes are there on each foot?
Draw lines to join the shoes to the correct feet.

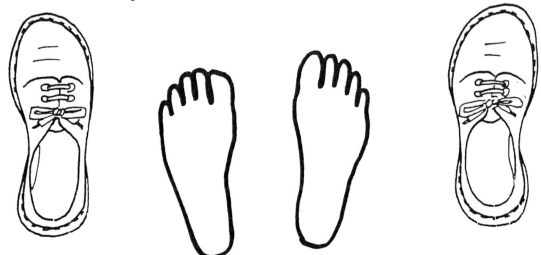

Draw around your feet. Are both the same?
Write left and right on the drawings of your feet.

Skin

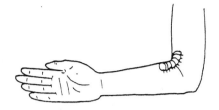

Paint a caterpillar on the inside of your elbow using face paints. Watch him stretch as you move your arm.

Arch   **Loop**   **Whorl**   **Composite**

Different kinds of fingerprints

Rub a pencil on a sheet of paper to make a thick dark patch. Rub your finger tip on the pencil patch so that it is covered with powdered pencil. Now carefully put a piece of sellotape over your finger tip and press. The pencil powder sticks to the sellotape. Gently pull off the sellotape and stick it to a piece of white paper. You can now see your fingerprint. Do the same thing with all your fingers and thumbs to make a complete set.

Food and water

What does Sam need?

Write or draw on the plates what you eat at these meals.
What do you drink? Write it on the mugs.

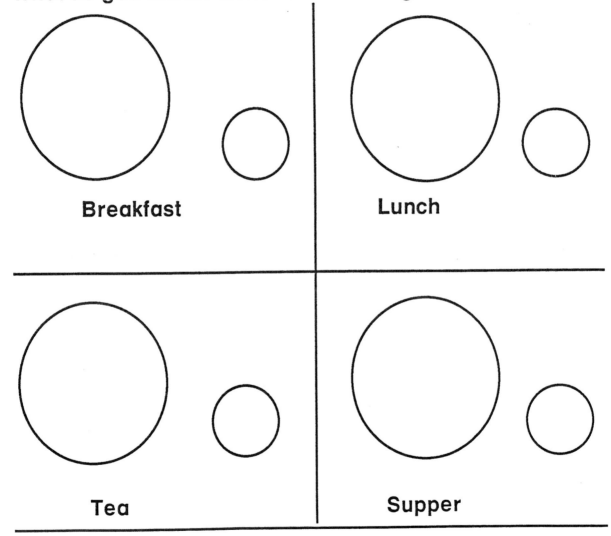

Breakfast

Lunch

Tea

Supper

What do you like to eat and drink best?
Keep a diary of what you eat and drink in a week.

Healthy food

Draw a ring around the food that is good for you.

You should not eat too much
of some of these foods.
Draw X on each of these.

You have a friend to lunch
or dinner. Is this a healthy
meal for your friend?
Give reasons for your answer.

Storing food

Draw lines to show where the food should be kept.

Draw a circle around the foods which are usually bought fresh everyday.

Why are foods sold in tins?
Find out how food is stored in your home.

Foods from animals and plants

Which of these foods come from animals and which come from plants? Write or draw them in the correct column.

egg

cheese

bread

milk
MILK

cereal

banana

fishfingers

jam
JAM

sausage

chicken

crisps

butter
Butter

chips

marmalade
MARMA

mustard
MUSTARD

honey
HONEY

olive oil
OLIVE OIL

tea and lemon

peanut butter
PEANUT BUTTER

biscuits
BISCUITS

foods from animals	foods from plants

Keeping healthy

You need to eat food.
Draw your favourite foods.

You need to drink.
What do you drink?

You need to sleep
At what time do you go to bed?
How do you feel just before you go to bed?
When do you get up?
How many hours do you sleep?

You need to run about and play games.
Do you feel breathless after running hard?
What happens to your heart beat when you are running?
What do you like best?

You need to wash and clean your teeth.
When do you wash?
When do you clean your teeth?

Medicines

How do you know when you are ill?

What illnesses do children sometimes have?

What medicines help us keep fit and not catch diseases?

How can we make ourselves better when we are ill?

What do grown ups sometimes do that can make them ill? How would you persuade them not to do these things?

Babies and adults

This is the Wilson family. Draw Mr Wilson and Grandmother Wilson.

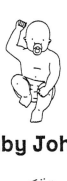

Baby John

Sam Wilson

Jennifer Wilson

Mrs Wilson

Grandfather Wilson

Kevin Wilson

Mr Wilson   **Grandmother Wilson**

Colour the family then cut them out and paste them on to a sheet of paper in order of age beginning with baby John.

Growing

These drawings show how tall Sam was on different birth-days.
Colour them, then cut them out and paste them on the chart.

1 year

3 years

5 years

7 years

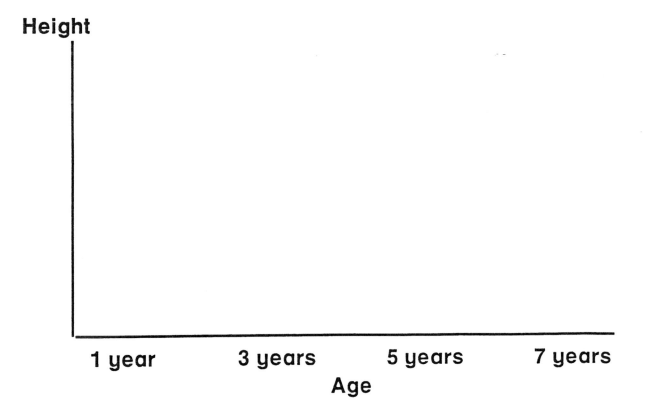

Height

1 year   3 years   5 years   7 years

Age

Now draw the same kind of chart for yourself.

Your senses

Draw lines to these drawings to show what you use when you

see   hear   smell   touch   taste

You can tell the difference between a wooden ruler and a metal one by looking at it and by touching it.
What senses would you use to tell the difference between the following? [You may use one sense or more than one in each example.]

A white rose and a red rose.

A piece of white paper and a piece of white plastic film.

A plain crisp and a salt and vinegar crisp.

The voices of two of your friends on the telephone.

Toast and kippers being cooked under the grill.

A pinch of salt and sugar.

Two songs.

Hot and cold water.

An aeroplane and a lorry.

Two books.

Touching

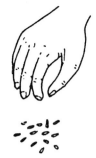 

Place a pile of grains of rice on the table and pick them up.

Now put on gloves and pick up the grains. Is it easier or more difficult to pick up the grains with gloves?

Which is the most sensitive part of your hands?

Place these objects in a bag. Blindfold a friend and ask him or her to take them out of the bag and name them. [You may be able to put different things in the bag.]

Tasting

Never taste anything unless an adult says it is safe to eat.

Dip a clean finger into some sugar and place a little on the back, side and front of your tongue. Where does it taste sweet?

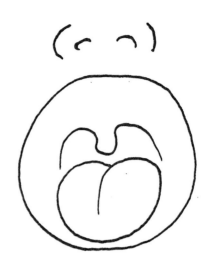

Rinse your mouth with water or drink a little water. Dip a clean finger into some coffee and place a little on the back, side and front of your tongue. Where does it taste sour?

For this you need two drinks such as banana and straw- berry milk shakes. Put a straw in each. Blindfold yourself and hold your nose. Taste one drink then the other. Can you tell the differ- ence between them?

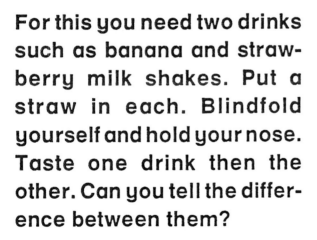
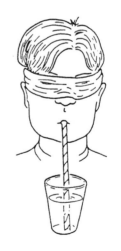

Can you explain why you cannot taste food properly when you have a cold?

Looking

Look at these two pictures and make a list of the differences between them. Which 'picture' would you prefer to live in and why?

Picture A Sleepyville

Picture B Sleepyville ten years later.

Fool your senses

cold   warm   hot

Fill a bowl with cold water, another with warm water and a third with quite hot water. [Do not make the water too hot.] Place your right hand in the cold water and your left hand in the hot water.

cold   warm   hot

Count to 30. Now put both hands in the bowl of warm water.
How do your hands feel? What is each hand telling you about the water? Is it hot or cold?

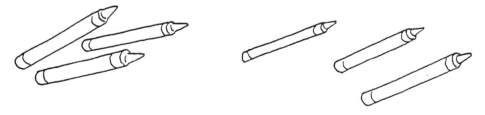

Look at several crayons in a very dimly lit room. Can you tell what colour they are? Look at them in a bright light now.

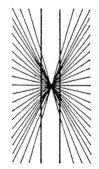

Are these lines straight?
Check with a ruler.

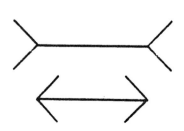

Which line is the longer?

Parts of a flowering plant

Draw lines to join the words to the correct parts.

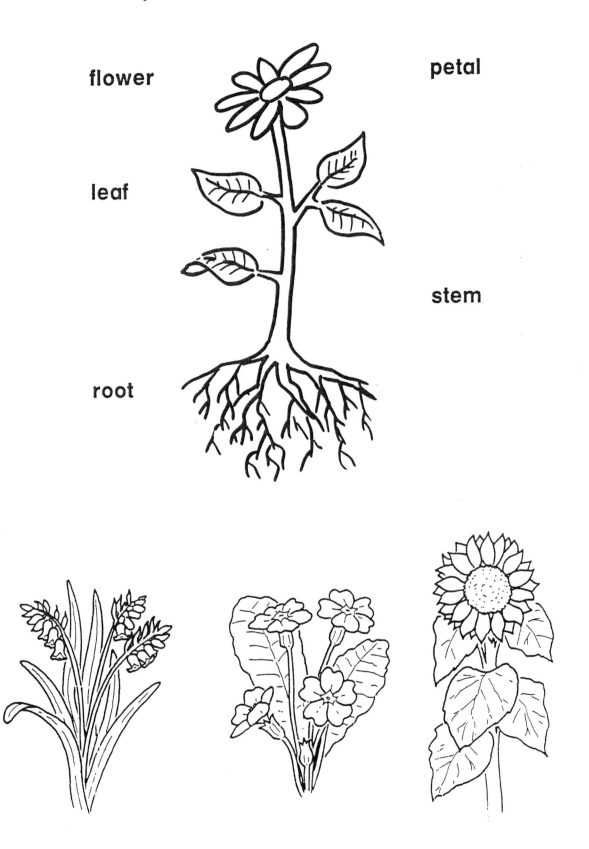

flower

petal

leaf

stem

root

Name these flowers and colour them.
[Choose from bluebell, primrose and sunflower.]

What plants need

Method.

Place some cress seeds in earth in three pots.	Draw the seedlings after a few days.
 Gently wet the soil in one pot and place it on a window sill.	Soil, light and water.
 Gently wet the soil in another pot and place it in a dark cupboard or a box and close the lid.	Soil, water, no light.
 Put the third pot with dry soil on a window sill.	Soil, light no water.
 Put some wet cotton wool in a fourth pot and sprinkle with cress seeds. Place this pot on a window sill.	Light, water, no soil.

What do plants need to grow well?

Plants and water

Fill a jar with water and add a few drops of blue ink.
Put a stick of celery in the water and place near an open window for a few hours. What happens to the leaves of the celery?
Cut a slice from the stem. What can you see?

Place a clear plastic bag over a potted plant and leave the plant to stand in a sunny place for several hours.
What can you see on the inside of the bag?
Can you explain what has happened?

Make a bottle garden

You need a large bottle with a lid. Place layers of pebbles or marbles, charcoal and damp potting compost inside it.
Then add a few small plants and sprinkle them with water. Close with the lid.
This garden should not need to be watered. Can you explain why?

Plants and light

Leave a pot plant to grow on the window sill for several weeks. Which way do the plants grow?

Cover one leaf of a growing plant with metal foil so that it gets no light. Leave it for a week. What has happened to the leaf?

Find out the name of the substance that makes leaves green.

Leaf prints

Collect leaves of different shapes. To make a print, place a leaf on a piece of hard cardboard or wood and cover with a piece of white paper.
Rub over the paper with a wax crayon or soft pencil so that the shape of the leaf can be seen. Always rub in the same direction and try using different colours.
Label each rubbing with the name of the plant from which the leaf comes.

Leaf fossils

Gently press a leaf on to a piece of plasticine. Remove the leaf so that the the shape and veins of the leaf show on the plasticine. Cover this mould of the leaf with self-hardening clay. When the clay has set, gently remove the plasticine and you have a fossil of the leaf in clay.
Label the fossil with the name of the plant from which the leaf came.
Find out how fossils are formed and why they are important.

Growing seeds

Line a glass jar with a piece of paper towel. Put a few dried kidney bean seeds between the glass and the towel. Pour a little water into the jar. Close the jar with its lid and leave it to stand for a week. What has happened to the kidney beans?

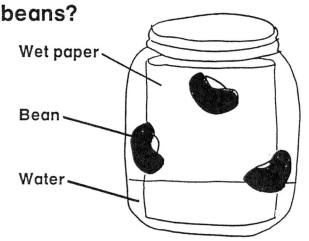

Wet paper

Bean

Water

Keep the jar in a warm place out of direct sunlight.

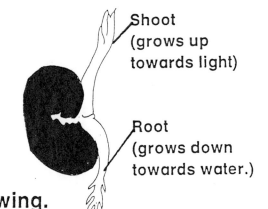

Shoot (grows up towards light)

Root (grows down towards water.)

The beans have germinated. They have grown shoots and roots and are ready to start growing.

When the roots and shoots are two or three centimetres long, turn the jar upside down. What happens to the seedlings after a few days? Draw one of these seedlings.

From seed to seed

It does not seem possible that a great oak grows from a tiny acorn. Plants produce flowers which turn into fruits with seeds inside. Seeds are spread in many ways. Some just fall to the ground and others are blown by the wind. Some seeds are carried on the furs of animals and rubbed off as the animals move about. Some seeds are eaten but not digested by animals and are passed out with droppings. When a seed falls on the right kind of soil, it grows into a seedling. This grows into an adult plant which in turn produces more seeds.

Can you complete this chart?

Plant	Flower	Fruit	Seed
chestnut tree	lantern	nut (conker)	nut (conker)
apple tree	blossom	apple	pip
oak tree			
cherry tree			
sycamore tree			
conifer			
		strawberry	
		tomato	

Use this chart to make a large wall chart. Add drawings and colour them.

Fruits and vegetables

Draw lines to show if these plants are vegetables or fruits.

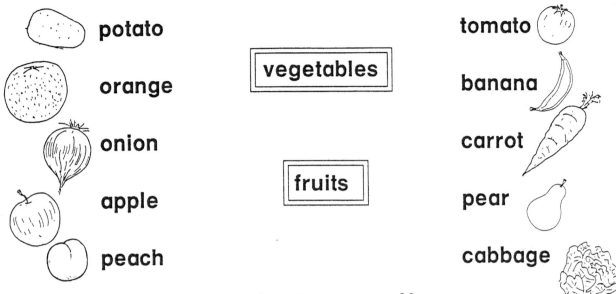

potato

orange

onion

apple

peach

vegetables

fruits

tomato

banana

carrot

pear

cabbage

Which of these grow under the ground?
Which of these grow on a tree?

Parts of plants that we eat

Draw a line to show which part of the plant we eat.

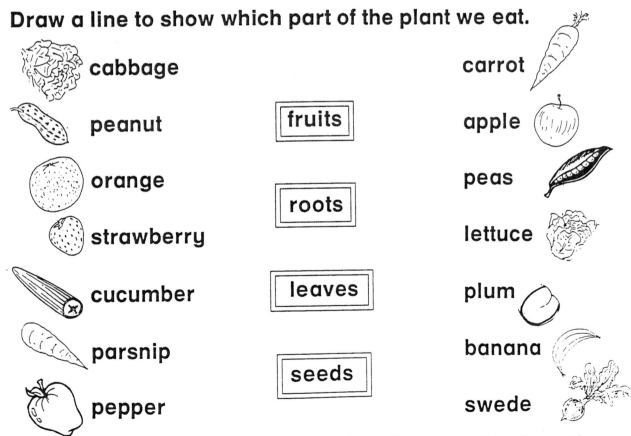

cabbage

peanut

orange

strawberry

cucumber

parsnip

pepper

fruits

roots

leaves

seeds

carrot

apple

peas

lettuce

plum

banana

swede

You are shopping in a supermaket. Draw and colour the
fruit and vegetables you have bought.

My class

We recognise our friends by their appearance - the colour of their hair and eyes, whether they are tall or short, thin or fat. Find out the colours of the hair and eyes of the children in your class.

Colour of eyes	Number of children	Colour of hair	Number of children
blue		blonde	
brown		brown	
green		black	
grey		ginger	

How else do you recognise people?
What other information about your class can you record?

Who do you think is the tallest in your class? How can you find out?
Who do you think is the fastest runner in your class? How can you find out?

Prepare a personal data sheet for yourself. Include your height, weight, colour of your hair and eyes, and anything else that makes you different from others in your class.

Draw and colour pictures of two of your friends.
Write a description of them.
How do they differ from each other?
In what ways are they alike?

Animals, insects or birds?

Draw lines to show whether these creatures are animals, insects or birds.

dog

elephant

owl

cat

fox

animals

fish

caterpillar

cow

frog

birds

snake

rabbit

beetle

insects

duck

rook

ladybird

butterfly

Habitats

Draw lines to show where you would expect to find each of these creatures.

mouse

butterfly

frog

ladybird

bird

seal

duck

shark

worm

pony

octopus

pig

snake

whale

owl

Minibeasts

Which of these minibeasts can you find in your school grounds?

Make a note of where you find each one and return it unharmed as soon as you can.

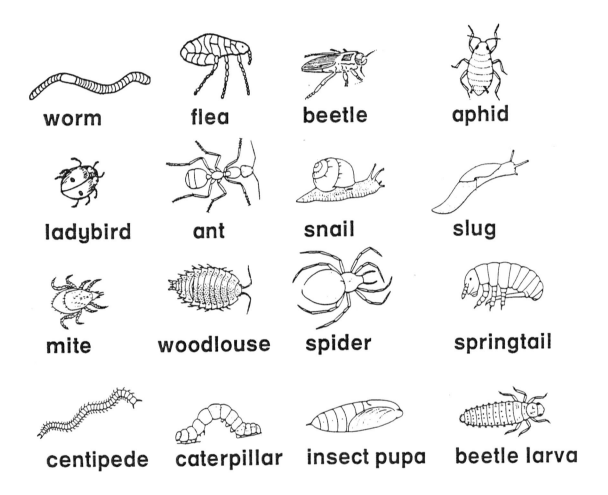

worm   flea   beetle   aphid

ladybird   ant   snail   slug

mite   woodlouse   spider   springtail

centipede   caterpillar   insect pupa   beetle larva

Draw any other minibeast you find.
Colour the drawing.

How does the minibeast move?

Describe the place where you found it.
Was it alone or were there a lot of them in the same place?

Find out the name of the minibeast and what it eats.
Do you know how to look after it?

Outside

Draw some of the animals, plants, flowers and trees you can find living together in the school grounds.

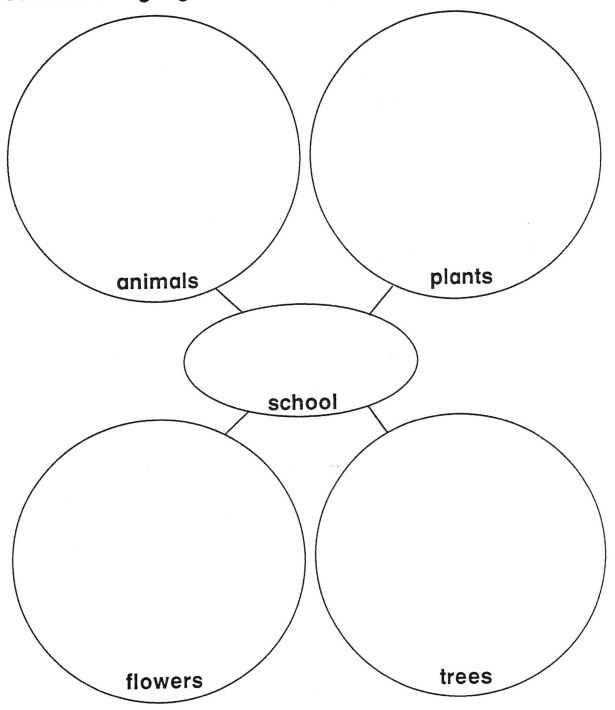

animals

plants

school

flowers

trees

Find out the names of the animals, plants, flowers and trees you have drawn.

Describe where they were found.

Why do you think they live together?

Feeding the birds

Place five dishes on the bird table,
one containing bacon fat,   one containing bread crumbs,
one containing seeds,   one containing cornflakes,
and one containing water.

After a few days put ticks (√) in this chart to show what the birds are eating.

food	none eaten	a little eaten	a lot eaten	all eaten
bacon fat				
bread crumbs				
seeds				
cornflakes				

Draw the birds that visit the table and find out their names.

Keep a record of when they visit the table.

Which birds like which food?

The wild patch

Keep a patch of the school grounds wild. Compare the animals, plants and flowers that live in this area with those that live in the grounds that are mowed and 'looked after'.

Date

Animal/plant	found	drawing/description

Life in and around a tree

Colour this picture and name the creatures living in or around the tree.

Use these names.

squirrel

owl

rook

millipede

woodlouse

fox

butterfly

lichen

woodpecker

wood pigeon

mole

hedgehog

toadstool

wood mouse

In what ways does the tree help these creatures to live?

Study a habitat in the school grounds or park and make a drawing like this.

Changes in the environment

Look at these two drawings of a farm. The second drawing
shows the same place 5 years later.

Describes the changes that have occurred.

What effects will these changes have on the animals, birds,
plants, flowers and trees?

What we do to the environment

These drawings show places where people live and work. How do you think what the people do affects the environment?

What we do	The effects of these activities on the environment
Live in towns	
Drive on motorways	
Work in factories and power stations	
Trawlers fish with small-holed nets	
Build reservoirs	
Use chemical sprays	
Use airports	

Decay of rubbish

Draw lines to show how you would dispose of this rubbish.
Colour brown the things that will decay naturally.
Colour green the things that can be recycled.
Colour red the things that will not decay and cannot be recycled.

egg shells

bread

glass bottle

paper roll

plastic spectacles

glass

metal car

Compost heap

banana

cereal packet

apple core

newspaper

beefburger

television

sandwich

Bin

tea leaves

plastic carrier bag

crisp packet

aluminium can

paper bag

Skip

sweet wrapper

broken chair

worn out shoe

potato peelings

plastic bottle

bath

oil can

Find out the kinds of rubbish produced at home.
What happens to it?

Decay of an apple core

To find out how an apple core decays in different conditions you need several air tight containers and apple cores.

1. Place an apple core in a dry, airtight container in a cold place or a refrigerator.
2. Place an apple core in a dry, airtight container in a warm place above a radiator or on a window sill.
3/4. Do the same thing with two more containers and apple cores but pour a little water over the apple cores before closing the containers.
5. Place an apple core and a little water in a dish and leave in a warm place above the radiator or on the window sill.

Conditions	What happened
1. No air, cold.	
2. No air, warm.	
3. No air, water, cold.	
4. No air, water, warm.	
5. Air, water, warm.	

What do these results show?

Cross out the unwanted words.
The apple core which decayed most had been kept cold/warm and dry/wet.

If you want to keep food fresh, how would you store it?

6. Bury an apple core in the ground and mark the spot. After three days examine the apple core. Describe what has happened.
Find out how rubbish is dealt with in your area.
Explain why rubbish is sometimes buried in tips.

ALWAYS THROW AWAY DECAYED FOOD WHEN YOU HAVE FINISHED THE EXPERIMENT.
ASK YOUR TEACHER WHAT TO DO WITH THE CONTAINERS.
WASH YOUR HANDS WHEN YOU HAVE FINISHED.

Decay of the environment

Look at these two pictures. The second drawing shows the school five years after it closed.
What has changed and why?

Materials

Draw a line from each picture to the word which tells you about it.

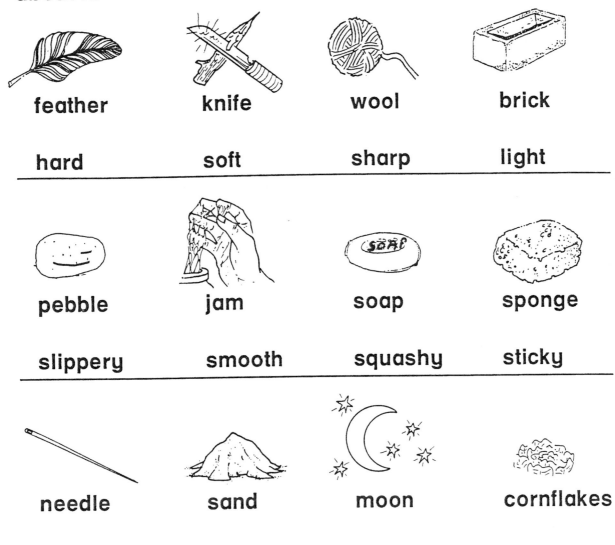

feather	knife	wool	brick
hard	soft	sharp	light

pebble	jam	soap	sponge
slippery	smooth	squashy	sticky

needle	sand	moon	cornflakes
gritty	shiny	crunchy	sharp

Draw a line from each picture to the two words which tell you about it.

legs	bread	snow flakes	boulder
cold	rough	hard	dry
fluffy	hairy	heavy	crumbly

Transparent materials

Draw a ring around the things that are transparent.

bottle	window	wooden door
fish tank	mirror	hand lens
book	spectacles	windscreen
glass	raindrop	metal foil
can	torch	china mug

Magnetic or non-magnetic

Draw a ring around the things that a magnet would pick up.

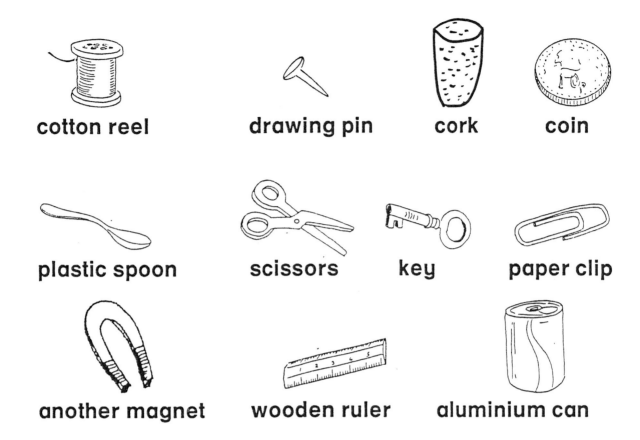

cotton reel   drawing pin   cork   coin

plastic spoon   scissors   key   paper clip

another magnet   wooden ruler   aluminium can

A metal paper clip has fallen to the bottom of a tall glass full of water.
Suggest how you could get the clip out of the glass without getting your fingers wet.

Aluminium cans can be recycled, others cannot. How could you sort out which cans in a pile of cans can be recycled?

You want to leave a message written on a piece of paper on the door of a refrigerator. How can you do this?

Natural or man-made?

Draw a line from each picture to show whether it is natural or man-made.

rock

sponge

newspaper

concrete

flower

natural

fleece

wood

oil

plastic bag

man-made

coal

water

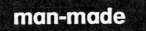

glass bottle

pebble

cork

Where does it come from?

Draw a line to show where the material for each object came from.

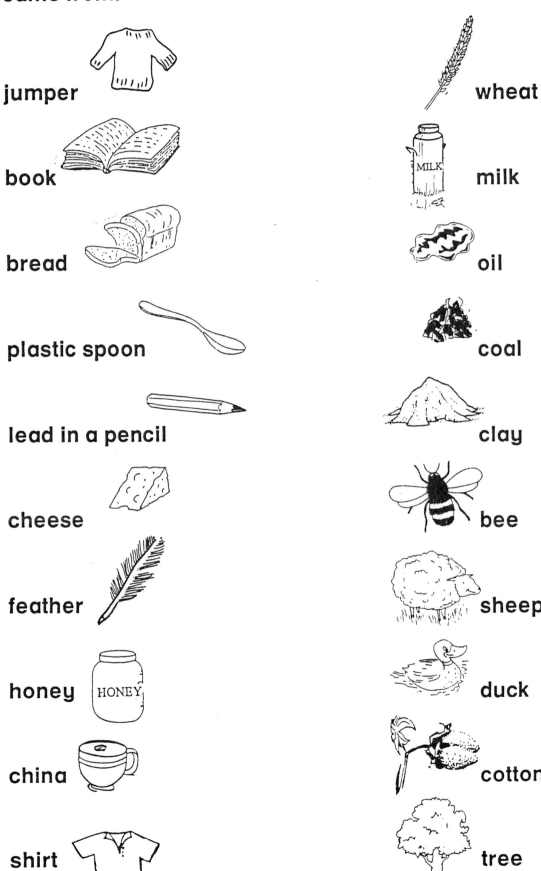

jumper

book

bread

plastic spoon

lead in a pencil

cheese

feather

honey

china

shirt

wheat

milk

oil

coal

clay

bee

sheep

duck

cotton

tree

Materials and their uses

Colour green the things made of wood.
Colour blue the things made of glass.
Colour red the things made of wool.
Colour yellow the things made of metal.

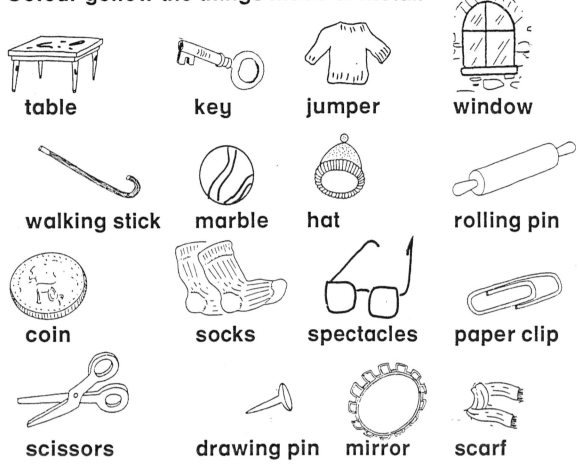

table	key	jumper	window
walking stick	marble	hat	rolling pin
coin	socks	spectacles	paper clip
scissors	drawing pin	mirror	scarf

This bottle is made from a material that is transparent, brittle and breaks easily. What is it made of?

This winter coat is made of a natural material that is soft, warm and was once alive. What is it made of?

This desk is made from a strong, hard, natural material. What is it made of?

This metal can is not magnetic. What is it made of?

Special uses of materials

Draw lines to show where these materials are used in the house.
Look for these materials in school and in the building you live in.
What is the scaffolding made of?
What are the two men in the bottom right hand corner of the picture doing?

slate

bricks

plastic

insulation

copper

glass

ceramic

brass

plaster

cement

aluminium

wood

Changing shape

Draw a ring round any of these that you can squash.

| tomato | sponge | wooden block | wool |

Draw a ring round any of these that you can bend.

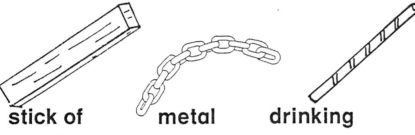 

| stick of Plasticine | metal chain | drinking straw | metal ruler |

Draw a ring round any of these that you can twist.

| long hair | rope | metal piping | metal wire |

Draw a ring round any of these that you can stretch.

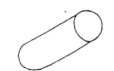 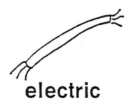 

| glass tube | rubber band | electric flex | piece of elastic |

What kind of material would you wrap around a pipe carrying hot water to keep the water hot?

Heating and cooling

Put some of each of the following into separate cups or tin cans. Place the cups or tin cans in a bowl of hot water. Which do you think will melt? Find out if you are right. Put a tick (√) in the correct column.

substance	melts	does not melt
butter		
chocolate		
candle wax		
an ice cube		
bread		

Place these substances in an ice tray in a freezer for about two hours. Find out which ones freeze. Put a tick (√) in the correct column.

substance	freezes	does not freeze
tomato ketchup		
olive oil		
chocolate		
butter		
cornflakes		
water		

Chocolate Krispies

Because you are going to eat these, be sure to wash your hands and that everything you use is clean.

You need a bar of chocolate, a handful of Rice Krispies and paper cake cases.

Break the bar of chocolate into pieces. Place the pieces in a cup and stand it in a bowl of hot water. When the chocolate has melted stir in some Rice Kispies. Spoon the chocolate mixture into paper cases and leave to stand until it is solid. They are ready to eat.

Chocolate Krispies can be made in this way because chocolate m . . . . when heated and becomes a s . . . . again when cooled.

Ice cubes melting

You need three ice cubes of the same size and three yoghurt pots or three tin cans, some kitchen film and cotton wool or kitchen paper towel. Find out how long it takes the ice cubes to melt.

Place an ice cube in each pot or tin and cover each with a piece of film.

Place one pot or can in a refrigerator.

Place the second above a radiator or on a warm window sill.

Wrap the last one in cotton wool or kitchen paper and place on a radiator or on a warm window sill.

Look at the ice cubes every ten minutes and write what you see.

	time	what I saw
can in a refrigerator		
can in a warm place		
wrapped can in a warm place		

Which ice cube melts first?

Water

What happens when water is heated?
[TO BE DONE BY AN ADULT ONLY.]

cold surface

What are these drops?

Find out which of these substances dissolve in cold water.
     salt, flour, sugar, coffee, sand, grains of rice, tea, detergent and
     biscuit crumbs.
Find out what happens when
you add each of these substances
to cold water and stir.

Put a tick in the correct column.

substance	dissolves	does not dissolve
salt		
flour		
sugar		
coffee		
sand		
grains of rice		
tea		
detergent		
biscuit crumbs		

Do you think your results would be different if the water were hot?
How can you find out? Record your results on another chart.
Now compare the two charts. Were your predictions correct?

Things that use electricity

Colour the things which use electricity.

television

garden swing

hair dryer

kettle

toaster

pen

candle

fire

lamp

spinning top

iron

hammer

washing machine

scissors

hang glider

vacuum cleaner

Things that use electricity

Colour the things which use electricity.

Dangers in the kitchen

Colour red all the things that are dangerous in this picture of a kitchen.

Circuits

Colour yellow the bulb that will light.

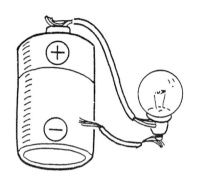

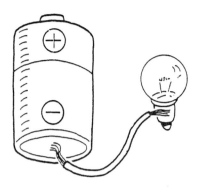

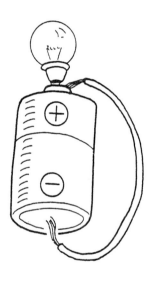

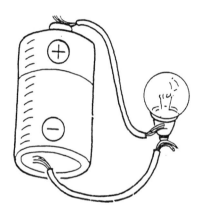

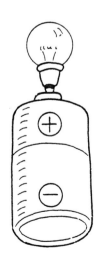

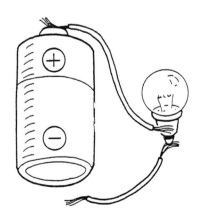

Conductors

There are different materials used in these circuits. Colour yellow the bulbs that you would expect to light.

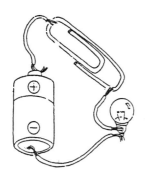

a metal paper clip

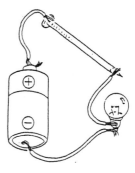

a nail

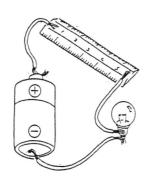

a wooden ruler

metal foil

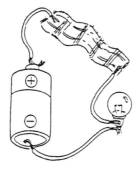

woollen material

a plastic spoon

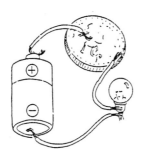

a coin

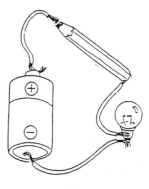

a pencil

Lights at night

Colour this picture.

Which things are using electricity to make light?

Batteries

Colour the things which use batteries.

TV remote control

fire

lamp

transistor radio

calculator

torch

television

hair dryer

clock

toaster

kettle

computer

mobile phone

toy fire engine

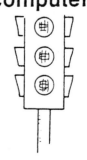

traffic lights

Changing speed and direction

These trucks are allowed to roll down the ramps on to a wooden floor. The ramps have different slopes.
Colour the truck red that will move the fastest.
Colour the truck blue that will move the slowest.

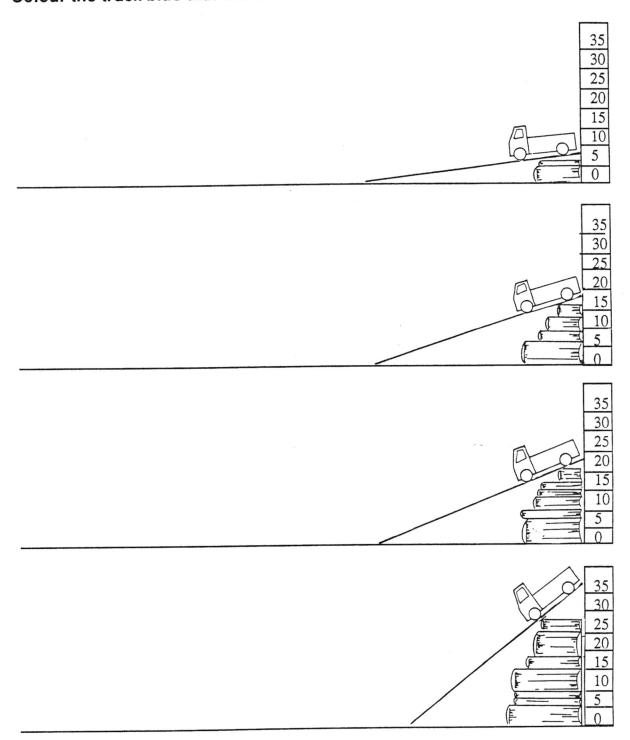

Draw arrows to show the direction in whch each truck will travel when it leaves the ramp.
Which truck do you think will travel furthest AFTER it has left the ramp?

Now try the experiment for yourself.

Surfaces and movement

When each truck leaves the ramp, it travels on a different surface. Which truck do you think will travel furthest AFTER it leaves the ramp? Which do you think will travel the smallest distance?

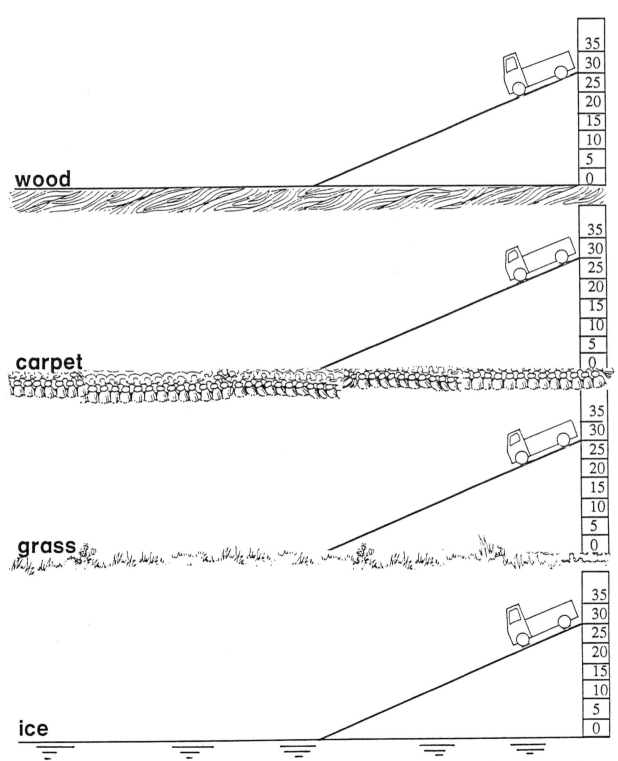

wood

carpet

grass

ice

Why do you think people should drive more slowly on icy roads?

Pushing and pulling

Colour the things that are pushed red and the things that are pulled green.

What happens when you stop pushing or pulling?

the buttons on a phone

broken-down car

wheel barrow

swings

brush

shopping bag

luggage trolley

toy truck

pram

Which of these trolleys is the harder to push? Give a reason for your answer.

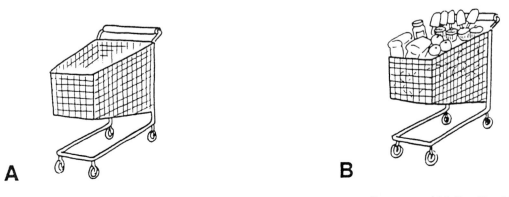

A

B

Floaters and sinkers

Put each of these objects in a bowl of water or in the sink and find out which of them float and which sink.

Then fill in the chart.

object	floats (√)	sinks (√)
wool		
wooden block		
plastic bottle		
cork		
key		
bread		
coin		
plastic spoon		
paper clip		
sponge		

Day and night

Shine a lamp on a globe of the world in a darkened room.
Which part of the globe is light?
Which part of the globe is dark?

Colour the part of the globe that is night in this diagram.
What happens when the globe is turned?

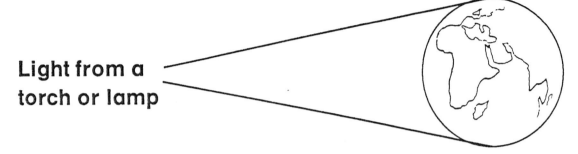

Light from a
torch or lamp

Earth, Sun and Moon

The Sun is a very big star which gives out light and heat.
The Earth moves around the Sun. The Earth takes a year to
go round the Sun once.
The Moon is small and goes around the Earth. It takes
about 28 days to go round the Earth once.

This is what William the astronaut can see. Colour the Sun
yellow, colour the Earth blue and green and colour the
Moon silver or grey.

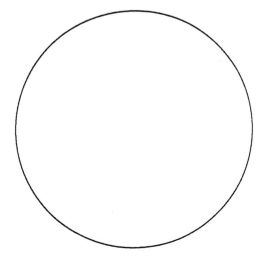

Light and shadows

NEVER LOOK DIRECTLY AT THE SUN

Make a shadow clock.

This is best done in the summer.

First, push a stick into the ground at 9 o'clock on a sunny morning. Mark the end of the shadow with a stone and write the time on it.

Do this every hour until school finishes.

Now you can tell the time by looking at the shadow of the stick.

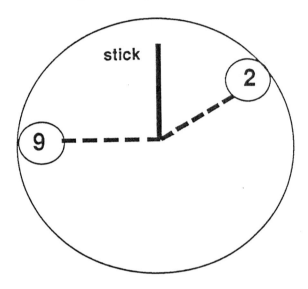

Look at your own shadow. Can you jump on it? Is it always the same size?

This picture shows the position of the sun in the morning. Draw the sun in the sky at midday and in the evening.

Seasons

What time of the year (what season) is it in each of these pictures? How do you know?

Draw pictures for the other two seasons in a year.

Picture A

Picture B

Name the seasons you have drawn.

The sun is shining, the days are getting longer and there are green buds on the trees. What time of year is it?

What is your favourite time of year? Give a reason for your answer.

What is the Weather like?

Make a Weather Chart showing when it is sunny, rainy or cloudy.

Write the days in the chart and name the month.

1	2	3	4	5	6	7
8	9	10	11	12	13	14
15	16	17	18	19	20	21
22	23	24	25	26	27	28
29	30	31				

Draw and colour these symbols or make your own.

sunny cloudy rainy

How many days were in the month?

How many days were sunny?

How many days were wet?

What do you think the weather will be like tomorrow?

Sam belongs to a club which meets on Saturday mornings when it is dry. How many times did the club meet in this month?

Janet visits her aunt on every other Monday. How often did she see her aunt in this month?

Crossing the road

Sam is crossing the road in front of the school bus.
Colour red the car that Sam cannot see.
Colour green the things that he can see.

Is this a sensible place for Sam to cross the road?

Pictures in the mirror

Use a mirror to see the whole picture. Then draw in the missing part.

Colour the correct reflection in the mirror.

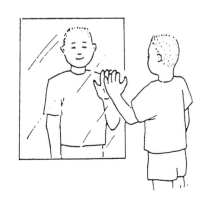

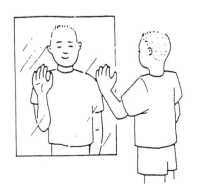

Sounds

Colour the things that are making a sound.

The police car is sounding its siren. How does Sam know when the car passes the window?

This class is listening to sounds outside the classroom. What sounds can you hear?

Making sounds

Colour red the instruments that you shake.
Colour blue the instruments that you bang.
Colour yellow the instruments that you blow.
Colour green the instruments that have strings that vibrate.
Colour brown an instrument with a keyboard.

Where do you hear best?

Sam is sitting on a chair and Jane walks slowly round him.
She stops in different places and claps her hands. Sam has
to point to where he thinks Jane is standing.
Where do you think Sam will hear Jane best?
Now you try the experiment with a classmate.

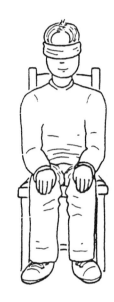

Make your voice louder using
a paper cone.
How does the cone affect your
hearing?

Cut this shape out of paper
or cardboard.
Fold and stick the edges together
with tape or paste to make your cone.

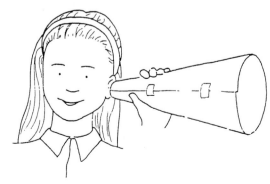

Vibrations

When something vibrates, it makes a sound.
Fold the paper over the comb.
Blow along the comb. Can you feel the paper vibrating?

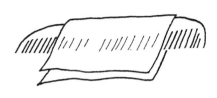

Look at the pictures below.
Hold the ruler on the table with a heavy book.
Make the ruler vibrate in different positions.
What can you hear?
DO NOT PUT YOUR FACE TOO CLOSE TO THE RULER.

Can you make sounds in other ways?

Echoes

Who will make an echo by shouting?

Jane   Sam

Can you make an echo?

Can you explain how the echo is formed?

Look at the picture below. Now arrange a watch, two cardboard tubes and a book as in the picture. Move the cardboard tubes until you can hear the watch ticking.

Do not disturb the tubes or the watch and carefully replace the book by a sponge. Can you hear the watch ticking now?

Can you explain what has happened?

Cock-a-doodle-moo

This sheet should be photocopied two or four time to make enough cards.
Colour the cards so that all the pictures of the same animal look the same. Paste the cards on board and cut them out.
Cover the backs with the drawings on the next page.

Shuffle the cards and deal as for snap. When two cards with the same animal follow each other, the player who first makes the sound of the animal on top picks up the cards on the table. The winner is the one with all the cards.

COCKEREL	CAT	SNAKE	DUCK
COW	OWL	DOG	FROG
PIG	SHEEP	BEE	FIELDMOUSE

Cock-a-doodle-moo backs for cards

This sheet should be photocopied two or four times to make enough cards. Colour these cards. Cut them out and paste on to the back of the playing cards on the previous page.

TWO BY TWO The finished cards can also be used to play Two by Two. The aim of the game is to find pairs of identical animals. The pack of cards is shuffled and the dealer lays out the pack face down on a table or on the floor. The person to the left of the dealer turns over two cards. If they are the same, he or she keeps them. If not, the cards are turned face down again. The person to the left then picks up two cards and so on. As more cards are turned over and replaced, it is possible to remember which are pairs. The winner is the player with the most pairs. This can also be played by one person who sets a target time by which all the cards must be paired.

Conservation dominoes

Colour the cards and paste them on to cardboard. Cut them out. Let the children design and colour the backs. The blank card may be any creature.

The cards are shuffled and spread out face down on the table. Each player takes four. The remaining cards are left with the picture side down to form the 'pool'. Play begins with the first player to the left of the dealer who can lay a double (two pictures the same on the domino.) The next player tries to lay down a card by matching a picture next to the first card laid down. The players in turn try to lay down a card to match either card at the end of the ones on the table. Cards may be placed in a straight line or at right angles. If a player is unable to lay a card down then he or she must take one from the pool. When there are no cards in the pool, a player must pass if he or she cannot match a card. The winner is the first one to have no cards left.

What am I?
Cards

These cards are part of the game on the next page. Colour these cards and the game sheet and paste them on to cardboard. Cut out the cards and use the sunflower backs (see earlier in the book) or the children can design their own.

This game can be played by two or more children. To start, place the cards face down on the table. One child picks one of the cards but does not show it to anyone. The other player or players then ask the questions on the board and follow the arrows until they guess which creature is on the selected card.

The child who makes the correct guess then picks a card.

The winner is either the one who makes the most correct guesses or the child who arrives at the correct answer in the shortest time.

Child

Squirrel

Owl

Sheep

Robin

Fish

Spider

Butterfly

Bee

Frog

Crocodile

Can you make another card for the game?

What am I?

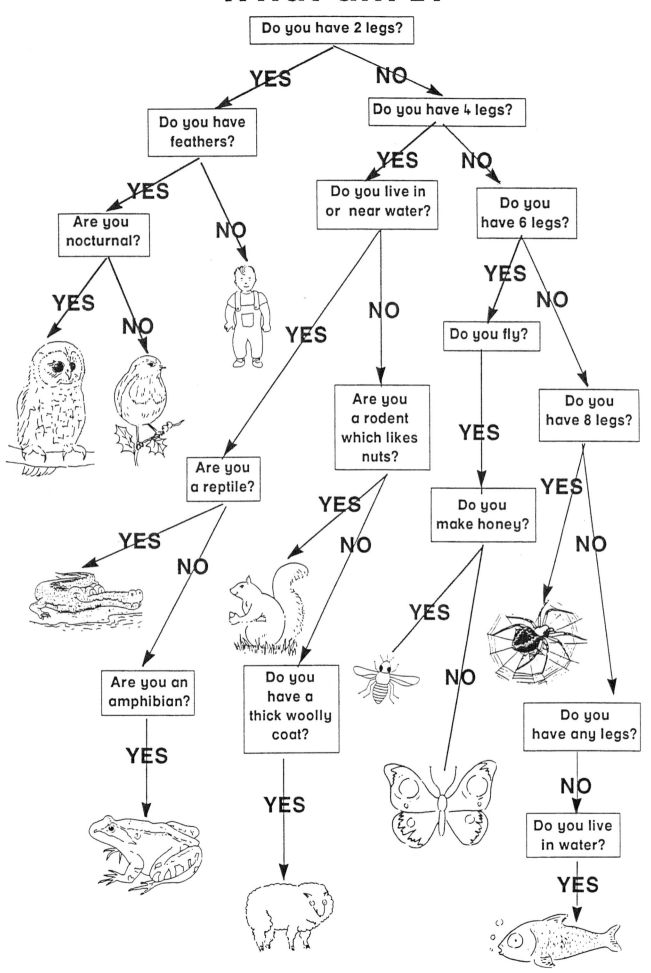

TEACHERS' NOTES
AND RESOURCES

To many of us, science is magic with explanations and some of the explanations are as mysterious as the magic: caterpillars become butterflies, iron ships float, raindrops make rainbows ... We communicate by satellite and mobile phone and despatch messages by fax and the internet. The very early teaching of science is perhaps the most important part of a child's development in the subject: at this time, a child can learn to enjoy it and find it fun. Attitudes developed here are likely to stay with the child for a long time - sometimes for life. Above all, teaching requires a love of the subject, imagination, patience and more patience. Science is part of our daily lives. We use it and expect a lot from it. We live longer and enjoy the benefits of advances in medicine. Regrettably, we have not yet learned to manage the excesses such as pollution and the destruction of non-renewable resources. We expect science to find solutions to our problems.

Children have always asked, 'Where did I come from?' Their list of questions may now include, 'What is a satellite?' or 'a CD ROM, a smart card ... ?' Today's children will live in a world where science and technology will increasingly intrude.

Teaching science is the opportunity to help children develop skills that will always be useful. The disciplines needed to observe, question, predict, plan investigations, record and use results are invaluable. The idea of a 'fair comparison,' essential to determine the importance of any one variable, is important at many levels. Fair comparisons are difficult to make in everyday life outside the classroom or laboratory. For example, it is almost impossible to compare prices of different brands of the same commodity in the supermarket. Weights and prices vary and packaging usually adds to the confusion. Similarly, pseudo-scientific advertisements often use jargon, slick acronyms and 'conditions' that imply much but prove little or nothing.

Children are receptive to the wonders of science. They enjoy looking at their environment, asking questions, finding out. When their enthusiasm is guided, progress is usually rapid. Girls should be encouraged to take an active part in science lessons on an equal footing with boys.

It is important to begin teaching a new topic within the child's experience. Build on this and gradually extend it. Always start with material the child can handle confidently. If there are difficulties go back to earlier work and the security of familiar ground. Sometimes extra time for play is needed. Never allow a child to stay confused or worried.

Science should be practical as much as possible. Hearing about what happens is not as exciting as finding out. Young children learn best when things have a reality that they can touch, feel and hold. Of course, at all times safety is vital. Children do not know that even a shallow pond can be dangerous, that steam scalds and that many berries are poisonous. Safe habits learned now will stay with them.

Some investigations require sensitive planning taking into account different religions and cultures. Be aware of the school's policy on sex education. Also some comparisons can be hurtful, for example, those involving personal qualities such as weight.

Science is fun. There is much to talk about, new words to learn, experiments, games and puzzles to try. At all times link what is taught with experiences outside the classroom, in the 'real' world, with 'real' work.

Children love to see their work displayed. Sometimes it can 'go home' to show to parents, who hopefully will appreciate its importance. As much as possible should be displayed in the classroom. It should be possible for everyone's work to be shown at some time. Displays should have clear headings so that everyone knows what they are about. Encourage children to draw pictures and later diagrams to illustrate their work.

Life is all about problem solving and so is science. Children love to find solutions and have more satisfaction from their own results than from other people's. Problem solving also develops social skills, especially when they work in groups.

> Children have to learn to work together, co-operate with each other, to listen to the ideas of others and offer suggestions of their own.
> They have to develop strategies, experiment and try out ideas, test theories and modify them.
> They have to use skills learned and concepts acquired within the context of the problem to be solved. This helps to reinforce the usefulness of what they have learned.

SCIENTIFIC SKILLS

The underlying aims of teaching science at Key Stage 1 is to teach scientific knowledge in such a way that the children develop scientific skills and a way of thinking that prepares them to work independently on scientific investigations. These are important aims, not always easy to achieve, and pupils acquire these skills to different extents. Some will find the disciplines more difficult than others. It is intended that

the children are required to carry out practical scientific work.
in carrying out this work, they acquire scientific knowledge.
the way in which the work is carried out develops scientific skills.
the children should develop a scientific approach to the planning of their work.

It is likely that the skills gained here will be important in other work.

It is essential that the teacher has a clear idea of the aim of each investigation and of what is being assessed. The work has to be carefully pre-planned and tried out. Teaching in this way with a class of 30 children of mixed ability is, to say the least, not easy. Keep the material as simple as possible and in manageable units. If too much is expected of the children, especially at the beginning, they will become confused.

Having decided on the topic, set the context for the investigation.

Make the question open-ended. For example, 'What is needed to make seeds grow?'

Children are familiar with plants growing. Once the discussion is started, they will make suggestions about what is needed by the plants.

Under guidance a list of possible requirements will develop.

The children may be able to choose for themselves which variable they would like to investigate or they may work in groups on different aspects of the experiment.

The amount of guidance needed about how the investigation should be carried out depends on the class: the age, ability and experience of the pupils. Too much guidance may hinder their development while too little results in confusion.

The equipment should have been prepared before the lesson. Often the equipment suggests how the investigation is to proceed.

As the children gain experience they will come to realise what is meant by 'fair testing' and begin to suggest ways in which one variable can be tested while all other conditions are kept constant.

Children learn to ask questions and to decide what to ask about the problem under investigation. As their skills develop, they will need less guidance although they will always need supervision. They will learn to draw on their previous experience and to use reference books to obtain information. They will also explore different ways of storing and presenting their investigations and results. Remember to display as much of the class work as possible. Many investigations lead to class results with everyone's work contributing.

When it is possible, science in the classroom should be related to science in the 'real world'. This is important in itself and also ensures that science is not thought of as an academic subject of little relevance to everyday life. Science is not a 'special subject, it is part of our lives. Some aspects are more clearly relevant than others. For example, the medical care we receive when we are ill and the ways in which we keep ourselves healthy:clean water, balanced diets, exercise and rest.

The children should learn that the balance in nature is a dynamic one and is easily upset. Their investigations should not disturb the habitats they examine, creatures should not be harmed and should be returned to their natural environments.

As the children gain experience they should begin to learn to use evidence they have collected and apply scientific principles.

Part of the teaching involves communication. This is an invaluable skill. Passing on information in a way that can be understood is not always easy. The pupils should learn the correct scientific terms to describe their work. They should learn to present information and results in different ways: orally, in writing, through drawings, diagrams, tables and charts. Children should learn to make their records as soon as possible. This encourages accuracy and ensures nothing is forgotten or left out.

Throughout their work, safety is vital. At this stage, children can learn the safe way of doing things, acquire good habits that will stay with them for always. They need to be aware of any dangers and know how to avoid hurting themselves, their classmates and any creatures they are handling.

Children learn to follow instructions. These must be clear and well planned.

SCIENTIFIC METHOD

The question forming the basis of the investigation should be open ended. In practice this may not always be possible especially in the early stages of the course when the children need a great deal of guidance.

Suggested answers to the original questions should start a discussion as to exactly what is to be investigated. The form of the investigations should develop from this discussion. From this should come a statement which summarises the aim/s of the investigation.

To carry out the experiment, the children have to know what they are looking for. They need to discuss what they think will happen and how these predictions can be tested. They need to decide what variables or factors they are examining. Arriving at this stage is not easy and a geat deal of guidance may be needed, especially at the beginning of the course.

It is important that the children begin to question their own suggestions and ideas: to consider whether the test or comparison is fair and will give a true result.

Having decided what they are going to measure or examine and suggested a way of carrying out the investigation, they have to decide how they are going to make the necessary observations or measurements. Then they have to decide how they are going to record these results.

Discussion about the equipment to use will probably have already started. Usually decisions about equipment and method go together. Making suitable apparatus readily available often guides the discussion and suggests possible methods.

Investigations should be written up as soon as possible. Often an investigation is spread over several lessons and each part should be recorded. The students should discuss the ways in which the results can be presented. They may use charts, tables, drawings ...

The children have to decide what conclusions they can draw from their results and if these results are what they expected.

Finally, they should explain what they have found out from the investigation.

LIFE PROCESSES AND LIVING THINGS

LIFE PROCESSES

Children need to know the characteristics of living things, to know what is alive and what is not alive. When this distinction is fully understood then they can consider things and substances that have never been alive. They need to know that animals including humans breathe, move, feed, grow, and reproduce. They will be aware that Teddy or a favourite doll may take part in games. Children talk to toys, 'feed' them, 'change nappies,' find them comforting companions but they are not and never have been alive and do not show the characteristics of life.

Children need to be aware of the things needed by all living things. At this age, they are constantly exploring and finding out what they can do, what parts of their bodies are involved in different functions: walking, running, climbing, swimming, and so on. Many have pets and it is useful to consider how their pets are cared for, what they eat and how they move. Children expect young animals to be smaller but easily identifiable editions of adults. Hatching chicks from eggs is a fascinating project for the class. Similarly, frogs from frog spawn and butterflies from caterpillars indicate the variety of life.

A walk through the school grounds shows that different animals live and survive in different environments.

Children know how they like to live. Similarly, animals need different habitats. At all times children should be taught to treat animals with respect, to disturb them as little as possible and not to hurt them.

Characteristics of Living Things

Breathing Watch how humans breathe and how this varies with exercise and rest. Watch how a cat or dog breathes. If possible show videos of other forms of breathing. Fish use gills to obtain dissolved oxygen from water while some amphibians have noses that can remain out of the water. Whales are very special and have blow holes. Plants breath and take in oxygen. A bottle garden shows how water vapour is given out to be re-used in photosynthesis.

Food Animals eat complex foods and break them down in digestion. Waste products are excreted while digested foods are used to build and repair tissue or to supply energy for the body. Plants absorb carbon dioxide and water in the presence of chlorophyll and sunlight to make carbohydrates. Oxygen is given out. This is the beginning of food chains.

Growth Animals follow stages in their life changing from babies into adults. Growth stops when they have reached adulthood. Plants grow throughout their lives although many have an optimum size.

Movement Animals move in a wide variety of ways from slithering, walking or crawling to swimming and flying. Their way of life and movement are closely linked. Plants move slowly by growth. They grow towards light and some respond to external stimuli such as the Venus fly trap if you feed it.

Stimuli Animals respond very quickly to stimuli. Plants respond slowly and usually by growth.

Reproduction Humans are mammals with the young growing in the womb and being suckled after birth. Birds lay eggs, fish lay eggs in the sea. Plants reproduce through seeds or through special organs such as tubers, bulbs, runners...

HUMANS AS ORGANISMS

Parts of the Body Children need to find out about themselves beginning with the names for the parts of their bodies e.g hand, elbow, knee ... Stick labels on parts of the body, play 'Simon Says'. Make a big drawing of the outline of the human body and label it. Associate different parts of the body with different activities. Investigate movements. The children may draw a caterpillar on their forearms and watch it move as their arms bend and straighten. They can feel the joint where the arm actually bends. In PE children can find out what parts of their bodies they use for running, climbing, crawling and so on.

Staying Alive and Healthy Children need to think about the things they need to stay alive and healthy such as clean water and good food, personal hygiene, exercise and rest. They need to learn about dangers at home, in school, in the street ... and how to look after themselves and watch out for others. They need to know what is essential e.g. food and water and what is necessary e.g. home and shelter.

Families Each child is part of a family chain. Make a family album and look for family likenesses. Features to consider include: hair, eyes, nose, mouth ... as well as character. Our bodies have symmetry with left and right sides. Children will happily put the left shoe on the right foot. Examine left and right shoes and gloves. Use

mirrors to find out if both sides of our faces are exactly the same.

Good Health This is a very important part of the course. Habits learned now are likely to last. This is also a very sensitive area involving different cultures and opinions. Analyse the habits of the class always being aware that the children come from different homes and backgrounds. Discuss the factors necessary for good health: food, sleep, exercise, hygiene - bathing, washing, cleaning teeth and washing hair.

Food is a very important part of good health. Humans are carnivorous while many animals are herbivorous and spend much of the lives grazing. Discuss a healthy diet and analyse what the children eat and what they like. Convenience foods are part of our daily life and the children will have lots of favourites. Collect labels and find out what is in the packages. It is surprising how often sugar is listed first as the main ingredient. Keep food diaries (for a day or a week depending on the class) and compare. Record pictorially or on a chart.

Discuss foods eaten at breakfast, lunch, tea, evening meal or supper and ethnic dishes. Collect pictures of favourite meals from magazines. Explain what we get from different foods:
Carbohydrates such as bread and cereals give us energy.
Fat is a very high source of energy and some is needed every day but not too much.
Similarly, **sugar** is full of energy. Be aware of 'hidden sugar' in foods.
Protein is needed for the building and repair of tissue. This is particularly important for children. The most important source is meat. If there are vegetarians in the class discuss where they obtain protein in their diet.
Vitamins are essential and found in fruit and vegetables.
Fibre helps to clean out the body -cereal, fruit and vegetables.

Compile a healthy diet identifying foods which are 'good for you' and those which should not be eaten too often.

Discuss how food should be stored and kept clean. Explain the need to wash your hands before dealing with food and to isolate uncooked meats. Explain that some foods need to be kept at low temperatures, that freezing food slows down the growth of bacteria but does not necessarily kill them.

Discuss the effects of bad diet and hunger. The causes are usually beyond the control of the victims - drought, crop failure, insects such as locusts, wars ...

Discuss the need for clean water: in many parts of the world people have to carry it for miles or drink contaminated water. Many diseases are water borne.

Drugs as Medicines Children will have experience of being ill. Discuss what makes them ill and what they do to get well. How do we know when we are ill? What medicines do we take and who gives them to us? Where are medicines kept at home? Why are they locked up? Discuss the use of preventative medicines such as vaccinations. This may be an opportunity to ask what adults sometimes do that make them ill e.g. smoke. Medicine is moving from treating diseases or their symptoms to preventative medicine and looking forward to maintaining general good health and well being. Play 'chemist shop', dentists, doctors and nurses.

Babies and Adults It is helpful and enjoyable if a parent is willing to bring a baby into school. Be prepared for children to ask all kinds of questions. Be aware of the school's policy on sex education. Within these guidelines it is usually best to give just as much information as the child has asked for and can understand. Compare the young baby with adults. Human babies are helpless for a long time and require a huge investment in time, effort and money. Most animals can walk independently within minutes of their birth: human babies take months. Compare how long it takes to grow up. Some life cycles such as the butterfly involve different forms. It is exciting to watch young animals grow. Stick insects will live on a twig in a glass cylinder, snails and fish can be bred in a tank. Guinea pigs are useful, they do not mind their young being handled. Woodlice and worms in a wormery give variety. A visit to a farm or zoo will broaden the children's view of animals. There are also numerous videos of animal life in different parts of the world.

Growing Look at the different generations in a family. Discuss how they differ physically and how they like to do or enjoy different things. Food, music and hobbies are usually good topics here, while soccer, rugby or cricket are often common links. Compare photographs of a family group and of one member at different ages.

Senses Collect objects that the children can describe by smelling and feeling. Blindfolded, children should **listen** to sounds, try to identify them and say where they come from. Explore the ways in which we are aware or examine our surroundings. Question whether our senses are completely reliable. Children can test their own **eyesight.** Compare looking with one eye and with

both eyes. With eyes closed, children should **taste** carefully selected substances. Discover which part of the tongue is sensitive to different substances and tastes. Fill a bag with a variety of objects which children identify by **feeling** them.

Discuss whether children like and dislike the same things.

Hygiene Make a collection of the things we need to keep ourselves clean. Discuss the importance of keeping clean. Discuss which parts of the body get most dirty. Children can try washing their hands in cold and then hot water, with and without soap. Discuss the different results.

Keeping Fit Pictures of sportsmen and women and equipment will interest and encourage children to take part in sporting activities. Discuss why people take part in sport. Find out and discuss what happens to the body during exercise: heart beat, breathing rate, temperature ... Keep a diary of time spent exercising and resting.

Safety at Home Discuss safety in the home and outside. Children could carry out a survey into how and where most accidents happen. Discuss where family medicines are kept and the dangers of taking other peoples' medicines. Plan a safety campaign and make a safety poster about the home. Discuss the household equipment that should be kept away from children. Discuss what causes adults to have accidents and what can be done to make the home safer.

Medicines Discuss why medicines are needed. Compare the illnesses that the children have had in the class and how they were treated. How do we know when we are ill? Discuss the preventative medicines and treatments for childhood diseases.

Life styles Keep a weekend diary and compare it with what happens on a school day. Which do the children prefer and why? Would they like to have 'weekends everyday'? Discuss a model day for different people. Nature imposes a structure for day and night but modern society imposes its own structure on this.

GREEN PLANTS AS ORGANISMS

Flowering Plants Collect a variety of plants and look for and name the main structures that they all have. Find out what is growing in the school grounds. Visit a wood or farm or city park. Look for the different structures for reproduction such as a runner, tuber and bulb.

Seeds Collect different kinds of seeds such as coconut, acorn, broad bean, and cress. Discuss how seeds are transported and the role of the wind and animals including man. Discuss dandelion seeds, sycamore seeds, nuts hidden by squirrels, seeds carried on the fur of animals, seeds not digested and passed out with droppings by birds, and agricultural crops. Find out how long it takes for seeds to germinate and the conditions needed for the seedlings to grow well.

Choose plants that grow quickly such as cress, or the spider plant. Discuss what seedlings are and where they come from. Investigate what is needed to make seedlings grow: growth medium, water, light, plant foods and temperature control.

Investigate different types of soil including compost and sand. Use different kinds of water such as rain, tap water, salt water and distilled water.

The children can plan their investigations and learn to keep all the variables the same except the one they are investigating. Discuss what and how they are going to measure what is happening, for example, the length of the seedling at the beginning and end of the experiment and the appearance/colour of the seedling. Discuss how the results are to be recorded, for example in a table, in a chart or on a graph. Discuss the drawings needed.

[Depending on the abilities of the children it may be possible to consider the experiment under the headings title, equipment, method, results, conclusion.]

Life Cycles Point out that the plant grows from seed (or other structure) and then reproduces so that the cycle is repeated.

Introduce the idea that food starts with plants: they take in nutrients from the soil and we eat the plants or other animals which have eaten them.

These cycles are delicately balanced and the destruction of one element can interrupt the whole cycle. Mono-cultures may be economically important but they can have adverse effects on the balance in the countryside.

Endangered Animals and Plants Because of the changes in the environment mostly through the activities of man, many living things are finding it difficult to exist and some become extinct.

VARIATION AND CLASSIFICATION

In a busy shopping centre, surrounded by hundreds of people, we have no difficulty in recognising people we know. Similarly, in school we know members of our class and would recognise most if not all of the children

in the school. Discuss the differences between different members of the class. This can be a very sensitive area and ensure that there is no cruelty or unkind teasing. Choose parameters such as age, birthdays, colour of hair, eyes, height, size of shoes ...

Similarities and Differences We have divided the animal world into classes decided by features common to groups of creatures. For example the way they move or their body covering. Thus, insects have bodies divided into sections and have six legs.

LIVING THINGS IN THEIR ENVIRONMENTS

Habitats Use pictures and videos to discuss different habitats and the animals which live in them. Discuss how they are adapted to survive in their enviroment. For example, polar bears have thick white coats to protect themselves against the cold and act as camouflage in the Arctic. Whales have a thick layer of blubber to protect them against the cold of the seas. Water birds have webbed feet and the camel, travelling long distances between oases in the desert, has a special store of fat in its hump. Animals with different lifestyles, e.g. herbivores and carnivores, have different kinds of teeth.

Adaptation The way in which an animal is built and moves determines the kind of food it can eat. Hunters like lions and tigers can run very fast, birds of prey like hawks and eagles have very good eyesight so that they can see their prey when they are flying.

Some animals live and hunt in packs, some live in family groups and some live alone.

A Particular Habitat Examine the creatures found in a particular habitat in the school grounds. Base the study on a pond, a corner in a playing field, or garden. Use a camera, tape recorder and note books. Children should be careful not to damage plants or hurt animals. Begin with a general description of the habitat - type, how much water or shelter there is ... Make a record of the larger animals that live there and then look for the small ones. Look under stones, leaves and in the grass.

Minibeasts The children can carefully collect some of the creatures in plastic containers and examine them using a magnifying glass. Discuss the conditions in which the minibeasts like insects live around the school - under stones, back walls and hedges. Observe the creatures in their environment. Consider if they all like living in the same places, how they move and how they defend themselves. Look for differences and similari-

ties between animals in the collection. Name as many of them as possible and classify according to some easily observed features such as the number of legs or colour.

The children can draw or photograph the creatures and describe the conditions in the places where they were found. Find out if the minibeasts like damp or dry conditions, light or darkness. Create a home for woodlice in a shoebox. It is important that the children learn to take care of the creatures and finally return them safely to their original habitats.

A Bird Table Carry out an investigation into the feeding of birds using food on a bird table. The children need to decide where to place the table. Keep a record of the birds that visit the table. Find their names using reference books. Note the size, colour, beaks, feet and feeding habits. The information can be used to make a large chart showing the birds, their names and what they eat. The Royal Society for the Protection of Birds, The Lodge, Sandy, Bedfordshire SG19 2DT, telephone 01767 80551 have a good teachers' pack which will help with this work.

A Tree Consider a tree or shrub. Examine the leaves and make a leaf print and press some leaves. Examine the bark and make a bark rubbing. The children need to learn to be careful not to cut or damage the bark because infections may enter the tree and even kill it. Record the changes that occur throughout the seasons: keep a tree diary.

Examine the life around and if possible in the tree. Discuss the ways in which the tree contributes to the environment by providing a home for creatures, providing shelter and shade, shedding leaves to enrich the soil, making the soil stable through its roots ...

Pond Dipping Special care is needed when water, even shallow water is involved with young children. They simply do not recognise any danger. Visit the area first and plan the excursion carefully. The children should wear suitable clothing. They can find out about the wildlife in the pond and around it. Dipping into the pond they will find a wide variety of creatures. Dip into the shallow part, the deep part, the middle, the edges, and any shady parts. Discuss which conditions are liked by which creatures. Find out how the animals move. Find out if humans have any affect on the pond. Make a plan and mark on it where the creatures were found.

The children need to know how to look after the minibeasts and finally return them to the pond. Their results can be recorded as drawings, tables, photographs or by video. The children should sketch the

habitats and try to decide if the minibeasts live there because they like the conditions and if different minibeasts like similar conditions. The results can also make an excellent poster.

Always encourage the children to predict what will happen and to suggest how they can carry out the investigation. They should realise that an investigation which proves a prediction to be correct is important but an investigation which proves a prediction wrong is equally important. A discussion to explain the results is useful and often leads to further investigations.

Plants in the Grounds Compare the plants in an uncultivated or 'wild' area of the grounds with those in a part that is 'looked after'. Discuss the flowers and plants found in the wild patch that are not found in the other part of the grounds. Find out if butterflies visit the wild patch and watch out for caterpillars.

Adaptation by Plants Plants too have adapted to survive in different conditions. For example, cacti in deserts have thick rubbery skins to minimise water loss.

Seasons Examine the changes that occur in response to natural variations such as the seasons. In the autumn, animals grow thicker coats, others like the hedgehog prepare to hibernate and squirrels store nuts for the winter. In the spring when the ground warms, seeds begin to germinate and green leaves grow on trees. Compare the different ways in which we dress throughout the year, how the food that we eat varies and how our lifestyles alter.

The Environment Because animals and plants are so well adapted to the environments in which they live, any changes in their surroundings may destroy them. Man changes his environment faster than any other animal and uses resources extravagantly to survive. When a biological niche is destroyed, species are endangered. Discuss the effects of the motor car, road building, aeroplanes, factories, power stations , farming ... on the environment.

Rubbish Find out the kinds of rubbish produced by the school and what happens to it. The children can find out what happens to the rubbish produced by their own families. Distinguish between natural and manufactured waste products, and between waste that can be recycled.

Sort according to type - plastic, paper, wood, metal,

glass. Sort the metal into magnetic or non-magnetic. What is likely to decay quickly? What will 'last forever'? Why are things thrown away? What materials are particularly difficult to deal with? What materials are dangerous if left to rot or just forgotten?

Examine the waste left in lunch boxes and discuss how it should be disposed of.

Decay Investigate the conditions in which an apple core decays for example temperature. Consdier if buried things decay faster and if the depth at which they are buried matters. The simplest way to record results is to describe the material at the beginning, at different times during the experiment and when the investigation has been completed. Caution is essential when refuse of any kind is investigated. Disposable gloves should be worn, hands should be washed when the work is finished and all waste products should be burned or disposed of when the experiment is completed.

Waste in the Environment Visit a park or waste land and investigate what has been left there by humans. Discuss the kind of litter which has been left there, how it will decay and its effect on the environment - on wildlife and people who visit the site. The children should be able to discuss the effects of waste in the environment and ways of dealing with it.

The class may be able to discuss other ways in which the environment is being damaged: pollution from cars, discharges from local works, use of chemicals in farming, noise pollution ... Beaches and seas become polluted and unfit for swimming. Rivers become poisoned by chemicals discharged into them and by leaks from disused underground mines so that fish cannot live in them.

Decay of the Environment. A school walk around the grounds or the neighbourhood will show plenty of examples of buildings, gardens and roads that have suffered from weathering, neglect or mis-use. Walls sometimes crack as they dry out or because of underground movement. Buildings that seem invincible when constructed succumb to the weather if they are not looked after. The school itself usually has some examples - paint on woodwork that is peeling, masonry that is crumbling and weeds breaking up paths.

Caves are formed by water containing carbon dioxide dissolving rocks. Cliffs may collapse because of the pounding of the sea and acid rain.

MATERIALS AND THEIR PROPERTIES

GROUPING MATERIALS

Children need to examine a variety of materials such as wood, plastic, metal, different fabrics including cotton, wool and synthetics, stone, concrete, rubber, soap, sponge, sand, rice, jam. Begin with the clothes the children are wearing. Most will have labels to confirm what the children think they are made of. Look at the things in the classroom from chairs and tables to books. They need to develop the vocabulary to describe them: rough, soft, hard, smooth, slippery, squashy, sticky, brittle, rough, scratchy ... A Feely Bag is useful with a changing range of substances in it.

Properties Some things can be identified by their shape such as fruits, vegetables, tins ... Similarly, toys have identifiable shapes. Discuss the reason for some shapes especially when there is a functional purpose: the relationship between shape and use.

Some materials are transparent. Make a 'stained glass window' from transparent sheets of coloured paper. Discuss the special uses and advantages/disadvantages of transparent materials.

Examine the characteristics of a wide range of materials such as wood, paper (from tissue to tracing paper, wallpaper and card), plastics (from thin carrier bag material to rigid heavy duty plastic), different metals, stones, coal, brick, concrete and china. Children should find out if a metal is magnetic or not. Depending on the ability of the class, useful vocabulary may include hard/soft, rough/smooth, dull/shiny, heavy/light, bouncy, rigid, waterproof, stretchy, transparent, translucent, opaque.

Kitchen Utensils The kitchen is the home laboratory and most of the equipment here has been made for a special purpose. Collect some of this equipment. Discuss the links between the materials and use of the items such as metal spoon, wooden work surface, wooden chopping board, metal saucepan, metal knife, plastic bottle, plastic jug, paper towel ... Compare the kitchen towel and writing paper for mopping up spilt water. Touch a warm (not too hot) metal spoon with bare hands then wearing oven gloves. Discuss what the oven gloves are made of, what special properties this material has and where else it is used in the house. Discuss also why fish and chips and ice cream are wapped in several layers of paper.

Other Materials Collect a wide range of materials and investigate their properties. Discuss how these proper-

ties affect their use. A visit to a building site or a walk around the school will show the different uses for different materials. Discuss how the materials used have changed and the advantages/disadvantages of the new ones, for example, aluminium window frames instead of wooden ones, plastic pipes instead of metal ones.

Natural and Man-Made Materials Materials such as leather or wool are obtained from animals and have been alive at some time. Man-made materials like plastics have never been alive. Similarly, minerals like stones have never been alive. The children need to know where natural materials have come from, for example, wool from sheep, paper from trees ...Examine a collection of fabrics. Compare their properties and discuss how they are used.

CHANGING MATERIALS

Shape The shape of some things can be changed by say twisting, or squashing. This depends on the the material used and the shape of the object. Thus, a metal can may be squashed easily.

Heating and Cooling Investigate the effect of heat on different substances. Candle wax is hard and brittle. When it is heated, it softens then melts. If the molten maerial is cooled, it becomes hard and brittle again. It is safe to allow a few drops of the molten wax to fall into a large bowl of cold water when the solid wax floats. (A large bowl of cold water is needed so that scalding steam will not be formed.)

Melt ice cubes and heat the water until it boils. Allow the steam to condense on a cold surface. The colourless water can be collected and tasted and re-frozen. This shows the change of state associated with temperature changes. The changes for candle wax and water are reversible (physical changes).

Compare with the changes that occur on cooking, for example, boiling an egg, baking a cake mixture. **Examining Materials** Look for colour, texture (rough/smooth, hard/soft ...), transparency, smell, flexibility (does it bend when warm?), strength (place a piece between two supports and put weights on the piece of material), stretchiness (does it stretch and then regain its shape?)

Dough Mix flour, water and yeast into dough. Examine what happens when the dough is left for different times and then baked for different times.
Jelly Cubes Dissolve jelly in hot water and then leave it to cool.

Weathering Look for discolouration, crumbling causing loss of detail on stone work and the rusting of metals. Consider the effects of weathering on buildings and on structures like bridges. Discuss the causes of weathering.

Consider the effects of weathering (and the sea) on cliffs and the importance of this.

Consider the effects of weathering on man-made materials.

PHYSICAL PROCESSES

ELECTRICITY

Children need to know that electricity is dangerous and that they should never touch sockets. They must understand that electricity can travel through their bodies and kill them. They should never touch anything using electricity if they have wet hands.

Making static electricity is fun. Let them comb hair for a few seconds. The comb will then attract tissue paper fish. Rub a balloon against a wall for a few minutes. It should then stick to the wall.

Uses of Electricity. A walk around the school shows the ways in which electricity is used. Children can discuss the ways in which electricity is used at home. Imagine life without electricity. Discuss the misuse of electricity.

Dangers of Electricity Electricity can jump through air and so it is dangerous to fly a kite near an electricity pylon. Make a list of dangers such as faulty flex, sockets near water, poking things into sockets, wet hands near electrical equipment, trailing flex, overloaded sockets … Make a safety poster.

Batteries They should be able to distinguish between things which use mains electricity and batteries. Some things, of course, can use either. Understand that batteries are a source of energy.

Circuits Let the children make circuits using a torch bulb, wires and a battery. They should find out when the bulb will light. They should also discover that the bulb will not light if there is a break in the circuit.

FORCES AND MOTION

Speed Children will be aware of cars accelerating and slowing down. They should be aware of the effect of speed, for example when cars have to stop. They can investigate the effects of slope on speed and different surfaces on how far a toy car can travel.

Pushing and Pulling Children will be familiar with pushing and pulling. They can try to push or pull a number o fobjects across the floor. Let some have flat bottoms and some have wheels. Sort into two groups - those that are easy to move and those that are harder to move. Discuss how they start the following to move: toy cars, skate boards, bicycles, scooters, pull along toys.

Experiment with a roundabout at a playground. Compare how hard it is to start the roundabout and then to keep it moving. What happens when they stop pushing? Examine how a swing works, how the movement is started, how it is kept going and how it stops.

Children use these forces in games and know that things which are pushed can often be pulled as well. Discuss which is the easier, pushing or pulling? Let them try pushing light and heavy objects. Is it easier to push an empty trolley or a full trolley around the supermarket? Discuss which parts of the body are used. Measure how hard a child can push by pushing against a bathroom scales.

Consider the relationships between the distance travelled and how hard it is pushed or pulled and the kind of surface it moves over.

Investigate ways in which objects can be made to swerve or change direction. Directing a jet of water from a squeezy bottle at a gently rolling ping pong ball should make it swerve and change direction.

Falling Compare the way a tennis ball falls when dropped from a height. Let it fall on to different surfaces. How high does it bounce? Repeat with a ball of plasticine. Attach the plasticine to a parachute and let it drop. Discuss the way in which it falls using different amounts of plasticine. [If children stand on chairs to drop these objects, be sure they are safe and cannot hurt themselves.]

Floaters and Sinkers children experience the force of water in the bath. Ducks float and sponges sink. A large bowl of water, a selection of items provides a good exercise in predicting and finding out.

LIGHT

Sources Consider sources of light such as the sun, electric light bulbs, gas lights, candles, car headlights and torches. Distinguish these from reflectors such as the moon amd mirrors. Examine a torch and discuss why there is a metal reflector behind the bulb.

Transparency Find out if light will pass though all materials. Discuss the uses of materials that are transparent. Include coloured plastic, cellophane and different liquids such as clean tap water, 'dirty' tap water, soapy water, cooking oil, milk.

Shadows Discuss what makes shadows. Let the light fall on an object from the side, top and bottom. Discuss how and why the shape of the shadow changes. Use a slide projector to shine a beam on a wall. Let the children make shadows. Let a child stand at the same spot at different times of the day and draw his or her

shadow. How does the shadow change? Make a shadow clock.

Children find it fun to jump on each others' shadows and discover that they cannot jump on their own.

Day and Night Shine a torch on a globe of the world in a darkened room. Move the globe so that it can be seen that parts of it move into and out of the light. Explain why there is day and night: while it is day here, it is night on the other side of the world. Discuss the size and positions in space of the Earth, Sun and Moon. Consider when it becomes dark early, when the evenings are light, where children play after school in winter and in summer.

The Moon Make a record of the shape of the Moon in a month. Discuss where the Moon comes from and why it shines.

What We Can See or perhaps more importantly, what we cannot see. Discuss whether light can travel around corners. Consider the dangers that exist because we cannot always see what is happening. Discuss the dangers of crossing the road and what senses we use when we cannot see everything because of, for example, obstacles.

The Brightness of Light Discuss whether we can see in all kinds of light. What happens when the light is dim, for example, at dusk? Discuss the effects on colours. What happens when we enter a room after we have been in bright sunlight for a while? Discuss why car drivers switch on headlights when they enter a tunnel in the day time even if the tunnel is quite short.

Animals Some animals hunt at night. Discuss how well nocturnal animals see.

SOUND

Begin by making children aware of the variety of sounds around them. Tell them to close their eyes and listen and then ask what they could hear. From these sounds, can they tell where they are and what is going on outside?

Voices Play recordings of different voices and animal sounds. If the people are known to the children, can they identify them? Often when people age, their voices remain almost unchanged and recognisable. Blindfold one of the children and let him or her stand facing away from the class and then try to identify any one of the class speaking. This is usually enjoyed by the whole

class and can be extended to allow the speakers to use accents or 'funny voices'.

Discuss the effect of one sound on another. Can they still identify the voice of a classmate if music is being played quite loudly at the same time? Do they always hear a sound such as the signal for the end of a lesson? Under what conditions might a sound be missed?

Familiar Sounds Discuss sounds that are heard at home. For example, what do the children hear before they get up in the morning? How do they know there is someone at the front door at home? Discuss the sounds that the children like and dislike. Are there sounds that make them feel secure or uneasy/frightened?

Animals Consider the behaviour of animals and why, for example, a dog often responds to a sound before humans or responds to a sound that humans cannot hear.

Noise What is noise? Does everyone have the same idea of noise? Discuss noise the children experience in school, outside and at home.

Loud Sounds Discuss what produces loud sounds. Are loud sounds pleasant? Discuss the use of headphones and the danger of having the sound too loud. Explain that in industry, workers have to wear ear muffs in places where the noise is too loud to prevent them becoming deaf. Discuss the dangers of wearing headphones in the street.

Direction of Sound One child sits blindfolded on a chair and another walks slowly around him or her stopping at intervals to make a sound (e.g. clap hands). The blindfolded child points to where he or she thinks the sound is coming from. Discuss if the sound is always heard clearly or if there is there a direction or position from which it is heard best. [The walker may need to be some distance away from the listener for this to become clear.]

Sound and Distance Find out how far away a pin can be heard dropping on to a hard surface and how far away someone can be heard talking before he or she has to shout. Make a telephone from two yoghurt pots joined by a piece of string. When you speak into one of the pots, the sound travels down the string and can be heard in the other pot.

Sound and Movement Discuss how sound changes when the object making it moves. Consider aeroplanes, trains, buses and cars. These are fast moving sources of

noise. Consider also footsteps and voices.

Sound and Air Consider how we can get rid of sounds that we do not want to hear such as the noise of traffic, roadworks and aircraft. Discuss the effect of wind on sound. [Our voices travel through air. Whales and dolphins communicate through water.]

Whispers Whisper the same message from one person to another. Discuss how and why the message has changed (if it has!) after say ten people in the chain.

Vibrations It may be difficult for children to understand that sound is produced by vibrations. Consider familiar instruments such as a guitar, piano or cymbals. Discuss the ways in which different instruments produce sounds: some are blown, others are struck, scraped, shaken or plucked and so on. Discuss how the sound can be made louder. Discuss the function of the sound box in a violin.

Hold a vibrating tuning fork close to the surface of water in a large bowl and watch the ripples. Tap against the school wall with the children holding their ears against the wall some distance away. [School railings are better for this than a wall but they can be dangerous unless they are very high. Children putting their heads near the tops of railings can injure themselves, especially since they may repeat the experiment when they are not supervised.]

Let the children make instruments. Stretch a rubber band over the hole in an empty tissue box and twang it. Pour some rice into a cylinder. Close the cylinder and shake it. The ways are endless.

Muffling Sound Turn on a radio and place it in a cardboard box with a lid and then in a polystyrene box. Discuss the ways in which unwanted sounds can be shut our of our homes, for example, how people cope with noise if they live near a motorway or ariport.

Making your voice louder Listen to a watch ticking using a stethoscope or a funnel.

Echoes Consider the sound of train anouncements in railway stations. Discuss why they are difficult to hear. Discuss other places in which echoes are formed and investigate sound bouncing off different surfaces.

RECORD SHEET
SCIENCE

Name _____   Age _____

Page	Master Copy		Page	Master Copy	
5	Living or Non-Living?		44	What We do to the Environment	
6	Materials		45	Decay of Rubbish	
7	Things needed by Living Things		45	Decay of an Apple Core	
8	Things I can do		47	Decay of the Environment	
9	Movement		48	Materials	
10	Parents and Babies		49	Transparent Materials	
11	Where do they live?		50	Magnetic or Non-Magnetic	
12	Me and Parts of the Body		51	Natural or Man-Made Materials?	
13	My Family Album		52	Where does It come from?	
14	Hands and Feet		53	Materials and Their Uses	
15	Skin		54	Special Uses of Materials	
16	Food and Water		55	Changing shape	
17	Healthy Food		56	Heating and Cooling Materials	
18	Storing Food		57	Chocolate Krispies	
19	Foods from Animals and Plants		58	Ice Cubes Melting	
20	Keeping Healthy		59	Water	
21	Medicines		60	Things that use Electricity	
22	Babies and Adults		61	Things that use Electricity	
23	Growing		62	Dangers in the Kitchen	
24	Your Senses		63	Circuits	
25	Touching		64	Conductors	
26	Tasting		65	Lights at Night	
27	Looking		66	Batteries	
28	Fool Your Senses		67	Changing Speed and Direction	
29	Parts of a Flowering Plant		68	Surfaces and Movement	
30	What Plants Need		69	Pushing and Pulling	
31	Plants and Water		70	Floaters and Sinkers	
31	Make a Bottle Garden		71	Day and Night	
32	Plants and Light		72	Light and Shadows	
32	Leaf Prints, Leaf Fossils		73	Seasons	
33	Growing Seeds		74	What is the Weather like?	
34	From Seed to Seed		75	Crossing the Road	
35	Fruits and Vegetables		76	Pictures in the Mirror	
35	Parts of Plants that We Eat		77	Sounds	
36	My Class		78	Making Sounds	
37	Animals, Insects or Birds?		79	Where do You Hear Best?	
38	Habitats		80	Vibrations	
39	Minibeasts		81	Echoes	
40	Outside		82	Cock-a-Doodle-Moo Game	
41	Feeding the Birds		83	Backs for Cards	
42	The Wild Patch		84	Conservation Dominoes	
43	Life in and around a Tree		85	What Am I? Cards	
44	Changes in the Environment		86	What Am I? Board	

NATIONAL CURRICULUM

MASTER FILE

MASTER FILES

published by
Domino Books (Wales) Ltd.

AN ESTABLISHED SERIES
prepared by experienced teachers

- NOTES FOR TEACHERS AND WORKSHEETS FOR PUPILS IN ONE BOOK

- COMPREHENSIVE NATIONAL CURRICULUM COVERAGE

- THERE IS NO NEED TO BUY ADDITIONAL MATERIAL

- ALL THE MATERIAL IS PHOTOCOPIABLE

- EXCELLENT VALUE

- SAVES YOU TIME AND MONEY

- VISUALLY STIMULATING

- BOOKS SPECIFICALLY DESIGNED FOR THE KEY STAGE YOU TEACH

- FULL OF TEACHING STRATEGIES AND IDEAS

- READY-TO-USE LESSONS

- FLEXIBLE RESOURCES FOR USE BY THE WHOLE CLASS, BY GROUPS OR BY INDIVIDUAL PUPILS

- TRIED AND TESTED MATERIALS

- PHOTOCOPIABLE SHEETS TO USE AS THEY ARE OR TO REDUCE OR ENLARGE

- PHOTOCOPIABLE RECORD SHEETS FOR EACH PUPIL

- NEW TITLES PUBLISHED MONTHLY

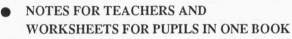

AVAILABLE FROM
Domino Books (Wales) Ltd.,
P O Box 32, Swansea SA1 1FN.
Tel. (01792) 459378   Fax. (01792) 466337
Telephone and fax orders welcome

ORDER FORM OVERLEAF

MASTER FILES
ORDER FORM

KEY STAGE 1 (Age 5 - 7) **KEY STAGE 2 (Age 7 - 11)** **KEY STAGE 3 (Age 11 - 14)**

Quantity	Title	ISBN	Price	Cost
	KS1 ENGLISH	1 85772 111 X	£20.00	£
	KS1 MATHEMATICS	1 85772 107 1	£20.00	£
	KS1 MENTAL MATHEMATICS	1 85772 154 3	£20.00	£
	KS1 SCIENCE	1 85772 108 X	£20.00	£
	KS1 HISTORY	1 85772 112 8	£20.00	£
	KS2 ENGLISH	1 85772 085 7	£20.00	£
	KS2 MATHEMATICS	1 85772 086 5	£20.00	£
	KS2 SCIENCE	1 85772 087 3	£20.00	£
	KS3 ENGLISH	1 85772 127 6	£20.00	£
	KS3 MATHEMATICS	1 85772 126 8	£20.00	£
	KS3 SCIENCE	1 85772 128 4	£20.00	£
HISTORY				
	KS2 Invaders and Settlers, The Celts	1 85772 067 9	£15.95	£
	KS2 Invaders and Settlers, The Romans	1 85772 070 9	£15.95	£
	KS2 Invaders and Settlers, The Vikings	1 85772 069 5	£15.95	£
	KS2 Life in Tudor Times	1 85772 076 8	£15.95	£
	KS2/KS3 Victorian Britain	1 85772 077 6	£15.95	£
TOPICS				
	KS2/KS3 Castles	1 85772 075 X	£15.95	£
	CHRISTMAS (AGES 5 - 12)	1 85772 065 2	£20.00	£
NEW FOR EARLY YEARS				
	First Steps Basic Activities in the 3Rs	1 85772 130 6	£12.50	£
	First Steps Number and Counting	1 85772 133 0	£12.50	£
	First Steps Beginning to Read	1 85772 138 1	£12.50	£
	First Steps Beginning to Write	1 85772 139 X	£12.50	£
	First Steps Beginning Mental Maths	1 85772 142 X	£12.50	£
	First Steps Mental Maths, 5 - 6 years	1 85772 143 8	£12.50	£
	First Steps Mental Maths, 6 - 7 years	1 85772 146 2	£12.50	£
	First Steps Mental Maths, 7 - 8 years	1 85772 147 0	£12.50	£
	First Steps Mental Maths 8 - 9 years	1 85772 148 9	£12.50	£
	First Steps Developing Literacy Skills 4 - 5 years	1 85772 151 9	£12.50	£
	First Steps Developing Literacy Skills 5- 6 years	1 85772 152 7	£12.50	£
	First Steps Developing Literacy Skills 6 - 7 years	1 85772 153 5	£12.50	£
	Reading and Comprehension 5 - 7 years, Book 1	1 85772 144 6	£12.50	£
	Reading and Comprehension 5 - 7 years, Book 2	1 85772 145 4	£12.50	£
			Total	£

Name/Organisation/School

Address

Post Code   Tel.

Contact   Signature

Order Number   Date

Available from Blackwells, Foyles Bookshop, Waterstones, Welsh Books Council, WH Smith, and all good booksellers or direct from

DOMINO BOOKS (WALES) LTD, P O BOX 32, SWANSEA SA1 1 FN.
Tel. 01792 459378   Fax. 01792 466337

All official orders must have an official requisition form attached (schools, educational establishments, LEAs, bookshops, libraries). Cheques with private orders please.